CW00411091

THE
CHRONICLES

of the Tiny Island

Only if you climb seven mountains of pain,
Cross seven valleys of sorrow,
Reach seven crossroads of despair,
Swim through seven lakes of sadness
Will the blindfold covering your eyes come off.
On that special day
Your heart will open up to receive,
And you will reach the meadows of happiness.
Looking back to the past
You will discover
That happiness was there all the time
As it was in
YOU.

THE
CHRONICLES

of the Tiny Island

ASH PHOENIX

For more information:
Ash Phoenix Trust
United Docks Business Park
Marina du Caudan, Port Louis
Mauritius
E-mail: permission@ash-phoenix.com
www.ash-phoenix.com

Typeset in India, printed in Mauritius.

ISBN 978-99949-0-734-2

For my family

CHAPTER ONE

The Rescue

Once upon a time, there was a young and reckless Lion who roamed the shores of a small island called the Tiny Island. The animals living on the island knew from the Red Fody that the Lion had not been born there.

She told them that one day, a lion cub had washed up on the shore on a plank to which he must have clung for many days, resisting hunger, thirst and the high waves splashing over his head.

Any other animal would have perished, but the cub was strong. A rumour arose among the animals that the lion cub must have come from Avaria, but he did not remember much about his former life. He had endured the dangerous journey across the ocean, and this was all that counted.

The cub was adopted by an unlikely couple: the Wise Cat and the Capricorn.

The Wise Cat was the high priestess of the Tiny Island. She was a master of the energy surrounding her, and a great healer who cured countless animals. She knew both the light and the dark sides of the energy of the universe but wisely chose the former, most of the time.

Even though she was bold and confident, she sometimes gave in to her fears. As we know, if that happens, the dark side becomes strong.

She was married to the Capricorn. No one on the Tiny Island knew where the Capricorn was originally from.

Some animals insisted that he came from the White Mountains, a place where precious diamonds could be found that were valued by many of them. Others suggested that he arrived on the island directly from Avaria—but these were only rumours.

Although the Capricorn was a healer and had cured numerous animals, most of them did not entirely trust him. It was whispered that he was a master of the black energy, but no one had proof of this. Even predators feared him, and not one of them dared to cross his path.

In the absence of an elected ruler among the animals, the Capricorn was an *éminence grise* who wielded his influence behind the scenes.

The Red Fody claimed that the Capricorn had not always been the Capricorn. She insisted that he had come to the Tiny Island as the Black Goat and had only later transformed into the Capricorn by jumping into the Underwater Waterfall.

The Fody was not only the oracle of the Tiny Island but also a wonderful storyteller. Hence, one could never be certain whether she was telling the truth or just one of her tales.

There was at least some truth in what she said. The Underwater Waterfall was pure magic. Nothing like it

existed anywhere else in the world. Other waterfalls fell from the top of a mountain and ended in a lake or the sea. This one was different as it flowed under the ocean.

A few animals argued that it was simply an optical illusion, that the sand on the seabed ran off in a way that made it appear to be flowing down a waterfall—but again no one knew for sure.

Some older animals claimed that an animal could transform their animal spirit by jumping into the waterfall, if they had the potential for transformation inside them. If that was not the case, the animal would drown, and no one could help them.

Sometimes, a young animal who thought they had a higher calling dived courageously into the Underwater Waterfall. Regularly, their dead body was found days later on the shore of the Tiny Island. Hence, only seldom did an animal dare attempt the transformation.

The lion cub grew up to become a beautiful, strong lion. So everyone called him Strong Lion. The Tiny Island was way too small for him. Although there were a few female predators roaming around, no other lion lived on the island.

Maybe, he thought, he would have to find his way back to Avaria to meet a lioness with whom he could mate and have cubs. Strong Lion dreamt of this every day, but he knew that he was young and still had time.

One day, as Strong Lion strode along the shore in search of prey, he saw a plank in the ocean. On the plank was a strange yellow-and-black-striped animal and a lion cub. The cub was jumping up and down and seemed scared. The other animal was just lying there—not moving.

As Strong Lion had a good heart and was also curious about the strange creature, he dived into the ocean, took the plank in his mouth and pushed it back to the beach.

The animal in front of him was unconscious and badly wounded on her left side. He could see and smell that she was female. Strong Lion immediately noticed how beautiful she was, although a little older than him. Her body was lean and muscular, and she was almost as tall as he was. The creature must be an apex predator, just like him, he thought.

The Lion realised that she and her cub must have been on the plank for many days—too many days. He carefully licked her wounds and dropped water into her dry mouth to bring her back to life. The cub followed his example and also licked her fur.

After what seemed like an eternity to Strong Lion, she woke up and opened her green eyes. When she looked into the Lion's eyes—a deep, strong and grateful look—he fell instantly in love with her. Although she was lying on the plank so helpless, so wounded, still she was so beautiful and strong.

'What kind of animal are you?' he asked her.

'I am the Tigress,' she responded warily.

When she was able to walk, Strong Lion found an empty cave nearby for her and her cub. He could not take them to his stepparents' cave as he did not want the Capricorn to know about the Tigress. Strong Lion did not trust his stepfather, who had mistreated him when he was little.

The Tigress recovered quickly under the loving care of the Lion. Every day, he brought her prey and licked her wounds. Eventually, even the injury where a white shark had attacked her while she was crossing the ocean healed, leaving only a long scar. Finally, the day came when the Tigress could again hunt for herself.

Strong Lion was curious and wanted to know everything about her. Although the Tigress was hesitant at first, one day she told him her story.

CHAPTER TWO

The Tigress and the Mountain Lion

The Tigress came from the Asantian rainforest. One day, she met an older Mountain Lion and was fascinated by his strength and agility. The Tigress followed him into the White Mountains, where she started a new life with him.

It was difficult for her to hunt there, but she was willing to give up her old life as she loved the Mountain Lion dearly. Soon she gave birth to a cub, whom they named Leo. He was more a real lion, like those living in the savannah, than a mountain lion or a tiger.

The Mountain Lion was intelligent, but he was also cautious. He did not trust other animals easily. Nonetheless, he loved and trusted the Tigress, in the same way she loved and trusted him.

The White Mountains were well known for the diamonds that could be found there, which were desired by many animals. As time passed, the Mountain Lion's focus changed from his family to the search for diamonds. With the shift of his priorities, his animal spirit also changed.

The Mountain Lion spent more time searching for diamonds and less time with his family. He became obsessed with diamonds and looked for them all day until he was exhausted. That was how he provided for his family.

Although it allowed them to have a luxurious life in a big cave, the Tigress was not impressed at all. She would rather have had the Mountain Lion devote his time to her and their cub.

One day, the Mountain Lion met the Black Goat in the White Mountains while he was searching for diamonds.

'Good morning, Mountain Lion,' the Goat greeted him like an old friend, but the Mountain Lion roared back. He felt uneasy with the Black Goat.

'I know a way you can find many more diamonds,' the Goat said with a smile. Instantly, he had the attention of the Mountain Lion.

'Yes, yes, please show me,' the Mountain Lion replied, trying to sound friendlier.

The Goat sensed his excitement and saw the greed in his eyes.

'Well, you simply have to go to the peak of the White Mountains, touch the Black Rock at the top, and wish to become another animal,' the Goat suggested.

'Why do I have to become a different animal to find more diamonds?' the Mountain Lion asked suspiciously.

'You need to become an animal who can climb better in the mountains and carry more diamonds,' the Goat replied. 'You will be so rich in diamonds that all the other animals will admire you.'

The Mountain Lion was not excited at the idea of

becoming a different animal. He loved being an agile, independent Mountain Lion. He loved his life; he loved his family and worked hard to provide for them. He needed more time with his family and not more diamonds.

The Mountain Lion knew this deep down in his heart. His animal spirit screamed at him that he should not trust the Goat. But ultimately his greed won out.

'What is the price for becoming another animal?' he finally asked. The Mountain Lion knew that a transformation into a different animal would not be free; it would have a price. Everything had a price. He expected the Goat to tell him that he would have to share the diamonds that he found.

'Oh, you do not have to give me anything. This advice is free. I give it out of admiration for you because I see that you have such a strong animal spirit. If you touch the Black Rock to transform, you will only lose your most precious memory,' the Goat answered, trying to sound innocent.

'My most precious memory? That is a lot!' the Mountain Lion replied. He instinctively knew that his most precious memory was connected to his family.

After some serious thinking about the consequences, the idea grew in his mind that he could provide even better for his family if only he had more diamonds.

The Mountain Lion noticed that the Goat had lit a black candle close to him so that he had to inhale its scent, which was strange and sweet and fogged his brain.

The last conscious thought he remembered was that

he had overheard other animals saying that the Goat used black magic. Until then, the Mountain Lion had not paid close attention to rumours about white or black magic—or, in fact, anything that went beyond the material world. He rather focused on those things that he could see, smell, touch and feel.

The Mountain Lion believed that his rational brain was superior to the less-developed brains of other animals. Magic was based more upon primitive beliefs than upon facts, he thought.

When the Mountain Lion woke up, he was lying at the foot of the Black Rock. The Goat was gone. The Mountain Lion could not remember exactly what had happened. His mind still foggy, he ran down the mountain. He stopped at the White Lake to see himself in the water, as his movements felt unfamiliar and his heart cold.

What he saw in the mirrored surface of the clear water was not a Mountain Lion but a White Wolf.

He was shocked and astonished by the transformation. However, he soon realised that as a wolf, he would be better able to search for diamonds. He would be able to see better at night and dig more efficiently in the dark soil at the top of the White Mountains. He smiled at the thought.

What he no longer remembered was his most precious memory. He had forgotten that he loved the Tigress and their cub.

As he was hungry, and the night was approaching fast, he made his way back to his beautiful cave.

The Tigress was taken by surprise when the White Wolf, who was unknown to her, entered the cave. She instantly roared and wanted to attack him. But when the Wolf howled back, she recognised the voice of the Mountain Lion.

'Why have you done this? Why did you transform your animal spirit? Why did you go to the Black Rock? It is black energy, black magic. You should never have done this!' the Tigress shouted in despair at the Wolf.

She had heard about the dangers of black magic— and that the Black Rock should be avoided at all costs. She also instinctively understood that a transformation into a different animal could have serious consequences if one's spirit was not strong enough to cope with being another animal.

'Why would you change your spirit and become a lesser animal? You were a strong Mountain Lion, and now you are a weaker White Wolf,' she added gloomily.

'Because I can find more diamonds, you stupid Tigress. Leave me in peace. Let me sleep now! I am exhausted,' the Wolf howled back.

'We do not need more diamonds!' the Tigress protested. 'We need only to hunt together as we did many full moons ago.'

The Tigress was tired of arguing and gave up the conversation with the White Wolf, who seemed strangely content about being a wolf. That night, the Wolf slept for the first time in a different corner of the cave.

The Tigress was deeply upset. She instinctively knew

that she had lost him. Over the next couple of days, she noticed his change of attitude towards her and Cub Leo. Realising this, she was even more devastated. How could she live together with a wolf, an animal who was known to be cruel and unjust?

For several nights she cried big tears, but with the dawn following her fifth night without sleep, she decided that she would stick by his side. She had committed to him for her entire animal life. The Tigress was not only loyal but also warm and caring.

The Tigress only slowly adapted to the changed nature of the former Mountain Lion and accepted that he was the White Wolf now. Although he slept most nights in a different corner of the big cave, the Tigress did not abandon him. She still loved him, whether he was a Mountain Lion or a White Wolf.

In the coming season, the Tigress focused her energy more on Cub Leo and tried to teach him how to hunt. She had to take down prey on her own after the transformation of the Mountain Lion, as he was no longer interested in hunting.

Instead, the Wolf spent all of his time looking for diamonds. He grew more obsessed with the search every day and neglected his duties as head of the family.

Now that he could collect more diamonds, their life was objectively beautiful. They were able to move to an even bigger cave. Instead of time and affection, he showered Cub Leo and the Tigress with valuable gifts.

The Tigress was determined not to give up on the Wolf. She wanted to help him transform back into the Mountain Lion he had once been.

In whatever free time she had, she asked other animals how he could change his animal spirit back into that of the Mountain Lion. But no one could answer her question. The Tigress' heart grew empty and sad because she could not help him.

Before the transformation of the Mountain Lion into the Wolf, they had done so many beautiful things together. They had visited a lot of places, for the Mountain Lion had taken her to the farthest corners of the world.

Once, they had even travelled to an island far away from the White Mountains. It was called the Tiny Island. In exchange for some of his diamonds, the

Mountain Lion had convinced a couple of eagles to carry them there in a net that could hold him and the Tigress.

The Tigress had loved the Tiny Island. They had stayed together in a beautiful spot where they had meditated and cleansed their bodies. It was called the Energy Point of the South. The Tigress had felt the spirituality of that place.

The Tigress had not wanted to leave the Tiny Island. She had wanted to live in cave close to the Energy Point of the South. However, as the Mountain Lion already loved his diamonds so much, he had insisted that they fly back to the White Mountains. The Tigress had been disappointed, but she could not convince him otherwise.

Most nights, the Tigress could not sleep properly. She lay awake and thought about how she could help the Wolf. One night, she had a dream that revealed to her a possible solution.

She saw the Wolf jump into the Underwater Waterfall of the Tiny Island and come out of it again as the Mountain Lion. In her dream, she saw him, Cub Leo and herself living in a beautiful cave near the Energy Point of the South. They lived happily ever after as the Mountain Lion's animal spirit was cured.

When the Tigress woke up the next morning, she vividly remembered her dream. She was determined to travel with the White Wolf to the Tiny Island so that he could be transformed back into her beloved Mountain Lion.

But things did not turn out as the Tigress had planned, because he was simply too obsessed with collecting more diamonds. Despite her many pleas, the Wolf did not want to go anywhere as he feared that other animals would collect the diamonds in his absence.

Fear was his new obsession—fear that he would lose all his diamonds or that they could be stolen. He carried all the diamonds that he had ever found with him. Every day, everywhere.

The Wolf no longer trusted even the Tigress. He grew increasingly tired because he even took the diamonds with him when he climbed the White Mountains. The Tigress saw this with growing concern. But she could convince him neither to leave them in the cave nor to take a few days' rest.

Then something terrible happened. While the Wolf was searching for more diamonds, one of the big bags of diamonds that he always had with him fell into a deep cleft in the White Mountains.

Over the next couple of days, he repeatedly tried to climb down the cleft with ropes. He even forced the Tigress to help him, but they failed because the cleft in the rocks was simply too deep.

But the White Wolf was not yet disheartened. He became obsessed with collecting new diamonds to make up for the loss of the bag. Instead of searching only during the day, he also started collecting them during most nights. He usually came back from his search only early the next morning. He became weaker every day

because he scarcely slept or ate. Yet he could not stop searching for diamonds.

One day, he decided to look for the lost bag one last time and went up to the top of the White Mountains. He was not only tired of his search for diamonds; deep down in his animal spirit, he was also tired of life.

When he came to the cleft in the rocks, he put a rope around a rock and climbed down. He never returned from the White Mountains.

Over the following days, the Tigress went up into the mountains and searched for the Wolf, but she could not find him.

Finally, she came to the cleft where he had lost his bag of diamonds initially. On the ground, she saw tools that belonged to the Wolf. There was a rope wrapped around a rock, but the rope had been cut. The end dangled loosely into the cleft.

Although the Tigress shouted his name for hours, she got no answer. She did not know what to think. When dusk came, she had to climb down from the mountains and go back to her cave, where Cub Leo was waiting for her.

So many questions twisted in her mind: Who had cut the rope? Was it the White Wolf himself? Or had someone else cut it while he was climbing down?

The Tigress had the feeling that she would never find out what had happened. She mourned his loss and did not stop crying for days as she missed him badly.

CHAPTER THREE

A New Life

The Tigress was heartbroken, but she was also strong-willed and fearless. She climbed down from the White Mountains that she hated so much and ran with her cub towards the shore of the ocean. It was a long, dangerous and tiring journey, but they finally reached the sea.

The Tigress was determined. She wanted to start a new life far away from the White Mountains, which had brought her no luck. She fetched a large plank, put prey that she had hunted before on it, took her cub and set off across the ocean. It was a dangerous trip, and they would not have made it if Strong Lion had not had the courage to swim to the plank and rescue them.

The Tigress and the Lion soon became a couple, and they hunted side by side. The Tigress was clumsy as she was used to hunting only in the dark rainforest and in the mountains but not in the open savannah. Strong Lion, therefore, gave her the name Clumsy Tiger.

The Tigress sometimes talked about the Mountain Lion and reminisced about the good times she had had with him. As she had a cub by the Mountain Lion, she decided that it was necessary to preserve some good memories for her cub. Leo should not forget where he came from.

This upset Strong Lion greatly, especially when she praised the Mountain Lion's strength and agility.

If Strong Lion had been more mature, he would have sensed that the loss of the Mountain Lion had hurt the Tigress deeply in her animal spirit. He would have recognised that she wanted to move forward by forgiving the Mountain Lion but that she needed time to heal.

As Strong Lion was a young and reckless apex predator who believed that no one could challenge him, he had a massive ego. He did not want any competition. He did not want the Tigress to think of any other male animal, even a dead one.

'You need to forget him completely, and you should not mention him in my presence,' he said to her. He even forbade her to think of the Mountain Lion and wanted her to erase all memories of him because he believed that this was the only way forward.

Strong Lion had a particular set of beliefs. It was difficult for him to think outside of the traditions with which he had grown up. This may have been because things on the Tiny Island always remained the same, and the animals were used to their ways of doing things.

He also lacked experience of grieving. One day, he even bit the Tigress because he could not stand her talking about the 'shadow'. She cried silently in her cave while Strong Lion was out hunting prey.

Clumsy Tiger had moved some time ago to a beautiful new cave near the beach, for which she had exchanged some diamonds.

The Mountain Lion had left a few diamonds in their cave before climbing up the White Mountains for the last time—something that he usually would not have done.

Strong Lion did not like the fact that the Tigress possessed those diamonds as he wanted to provide for her.

To cut a long story short, Strong Lion wanted to make Clumsy Tiger his queen, his lioness. What he did not realise, however, was that she was a free and independent Tigress who belonged in the Asantian rainforest and not on a small island.

The Tiny Island was too tiny for the Tigress, just as it was too small for the Lion, but he loved it there because he could hunt without restrictions and every other animal bowed before him.

One day, Clumsy Tiger heard from the Giant Eagle, who had crossed the ocean many times, that her mother, the Old Tigress, was ill. She decided to leave the island for a while to be with her mother. The Old Tigress recovered quickly, and Clumsy Tiger soon came back to be with Strong Lion.

The first few days were a happy reunion. But after they had spent these days together in joy, the Lion suddenly declared that he wanted to find his lioness and have two lion cubs of his own and three coyotes as his followers.

Strong Lion told Clumsy Tiger that he was going to leave her. She would have to cope on the Tiny Island on her own from now on or go back to the Asantian rainforest.

When he left her cave, he gave her a letter. In it, he expressed his feelings and thoughts so that Clumsy Tiger might better understand why they had to part ways.

Dear Clumsy Tiger,

Your Strong Lion is facing the biggest dilemma a lion can have at the moment. He has to choose between his rational brain and his emotional heart, and he is absolutely lost. He knows that there is no other Tigress like her on the island or even back in Asantia as she is one of a kind— an apex predator on the verge of extinction.

The Tigress has so many good qualities of which Strong Lion is in awe, and which he came to admire as he got to know her better. Strong Lion wishes to learn so much more from her. He knows that when they are together, they can hunt and fight the world side by side and feel protected by each other's love.

However, Strong Lion can still smell the old Mountain Lion on her and cannot bear that smell. He tried hard to ignore it, but his nose is just too sensitive to it. It is so delicate that he can even smell two other animals who fell prey to the Tigress, a young dodo and a donkey. They were no match for the Tigress, though, and she knows it was a stupid hunt for her.

The beautiful Tigress knows that she needs a real hunter by her side who can be there for her and Cub Leo.

She even likes the macho side of Strong Lion, although she will never admit it as she somehow wants equality between females and males, and this makes no sense to Strong Lion as an argument. He is not even that macho and often shows his soft, emotional side to her.

Strong Lion sometimes wishes that the Tigress would stop roaring so much at him and allow him to roar with her. He is starting to think that her trauma from the White Mountains may be the reason she cannot listen as well as him.

For the sake of them as a couple, but also for her survival in a world full of dangerous animals, he should from now on convince her that listening is key in the savannah.

There are other predator animals on the Tiny Island, like leopards, cheetahs, wolves and panthers. Strong Lion met a female black panther for one meal as friends.

Strong Lion will be there for the beautiful Tigress. She will need help until she decides whether she wants to move back to the Asantian rainforest or whether she can start loving herself enough that she becomes happy anywhere.

Strong Lion

Clumsy Tiger was hurt and heartbroken. She had enjoyed herself so much in the rainforest, where she could hunt without limits.

But she loved the Lion so deeply that she had decided to come back to the Tiny Island to be together with him, even if it meant that she would only be able to hunt small animals in the savannah.

Clumsy Tiger thought intensely about how she should proceed—whether she should go back to the Asantian rainforest or stay on the Tiny Island.

As Strong Lion had written in his letter, he was facing a dilemma—but in the Tigress' view, it was a choice between tradition, pride and logic on one side and love on the other.

His stepmother gave him a hard time about being with the Tigress. The Wise Cat told him that a lion was not made for a tiger and that he should seek a companion who would follow his lead, even if he could not find a lioness on the island.

His stepfather, the Capricorn, simply made him fearful. Strong Lion knew that he would lose all credibility in the Capricorn's eyes if he mated with the Tigress, who had a cub of her own. He hated the Capricorn so much that he needed to prove to him that he had the potential to become the future ruler of the Tiny Island.

As Strong Lion pointed out, there were other predators on the island. Somehow, Clumsy Tiger instinctively knew that he was still in search of his lioness with whom he could have the cubs he had always dreamt of. But for now, she put that thought aside. Instead, she started stubbornly to grieve their lost love.

Even though she had known deep inside that the connection between the Lion and her might not last for ever, she wanted to be with him, and his absence hurt her profoundly.

CHAPTER FOUR

Hunting Together Again

A few days later, Strong Lion visited Clumsy Tiger in her cave. He wanted to explain to Cub Leo why he and the Tigress had to go their separate ways. The cub looked up to the Lion. He copied him and even told his mother that he wanted to be just like Strong Lion when he grew up.

When the Lion came to the Tigress' cave and greeted her, he looked intensely into her green eyes, and Clumsy Tiger looked deep into his eyes.

Although neither would admit it, they instantly knew that they wanted to be together again. There was no question about it. And when, after a few days, Strong Lion once more visited the Tigress, they reconciled and resumed hunting side by side.

Time passed, and being together was bliss for them. They enjoyed each other's company, although they still roared at each other from time to time.

One day, Strong Lion decided to show Clumsy Tiger the magnificent Blue Bay. It was a beautiful lagoon. The water was clear and shimmered in many blue and turquoise shades. The Tigress was fascinated as she had never seen such a colourful lagoon before.

They both went swimming, and with their strong strokes, they quickly crossed from one side of the Blue Bay to the other.

When they reached the shallow waters on the other side, something unexpected happened. A Golden Watersnake slowly wrapped herself around the left paw of the Tigress.

'Go away, and leave Clumsy Tiger in peace,' the Lion roared at the Watersnake and quickly came to stand beside his Tigress. He was scared that the Golden Watersnake would bite Clumsy Tiger as he was not sure whether she was deadly poisonous or not.

'Do not be afraid, Strong Lion, I mean no harm. I have seen you two together, and I am happy to see that the love between you bridges the gap between different animal species.

'You both are mystical creatures—you, Tigress, are the empress of the rainforest, and you, Strong Lion, the ruler of the savannah. But I have also felt that your spirits are strongly connected to each other. Let me make you a gift that will seal your bond for ever,' the Watersnake said.

Strong Lion was confused, but before he could roar again, the Watersnake had wrapped her tail around his right paw. Both Clumsy Tiger and Strong Lion instantly experienced inner peace and serenity. They were united in love and felt as if the universe had opened up for a short moment for them to see beyond into their future.

The Golden Watersnake lit up brightly. A flash of light passed from Clumsy Tiger to Strong Lion and back. Then the Watersnake was gone. The Tigress and the Lion were now connected spiritually, and their life cords were deeply intertwined.

They were both speechless. Silently, they got out of the water, exhausted, and lay down on the beach beside the Blue Bay. They were so tired that they fell asleep immediately. And they both had the same dream.

They saw the wounded Lion and a White Tigress diving together into a lake. After a while, a majestic White Dragon came out of the lake and flew into the blue sky.

CHAPTER FIVE

The Curse of the Capricorn

The life of the two lovers took an unexpected turn instead of a happily-ever-after. Two independent and yet somehow related events changed the fate of the happy couple.

Both the Tigress and the Lion loved swimming. The weather on the Tiny Island had, however, changed recently. Although it was still mild, it was wintertime, with gusty winds blowing from the sea. The water was relatively cold. Strong Lion, like most other land animals, avoided swimming in the ocean.

Clumsy Tiger had no experience of winter on the Tiny Island, though. One day, she went swimming without the Lion. The Tigress was shivering when she headed back to her cave, as the wind was chilly that day.

The next day, she had high fever and a cough. She was seriously ill, and it was hard for her to care for Cub Leo. But Strong Lion came to her cave every day. He brought her healing medicine from the Wise Cat, and he stayed with her most of the time. Clumsy Tiger was happy and grateful that he was looking after her so well.

The care that Strong Lion showed to the Tigress triggered the jealousy of the Wise Cat. She did not like it at all that the Lion spent so much time with the Tigress and that he cared for her so deeply.

Partly, her concerns were caused by envy; partly, they were the worries of a protective stepmother. Even though she had adopted Strong Lion as a cub, she treated him as if he were her own and she loved him dearly.

In particular, she did not like the fact that she had never met Clumsy Tiger. Not once had the Tigress visited the Wise Cat, although she must have understood that it was impolite not to do so. The Tigress knew that many animals regarded the connection between the Lion and her as 'unnatural'. She expected the Wise Cat to be sceptical as well and therefore avoided visiting.

Even though Strong Lion talked a lot with his stepmother about the Tigress, not having met her even once annoyed the Wise Cat. She thought that Clumsy Tiger was arrogant.

Although the Wise Cat was usually wise, she was indeed prejudiced against the bond between her stepson and the Tigress. It was not healthy in her eyes. She doubted that the connection would be long-lasting, and she did not want Strong Lion's heart to be broken, as he had already suffered enough as a cub.

The Wise Cat was also anxious about what would happen if the Capricorn learned about them being a couple. She feared that the Capricorn might see their union as a threat to the influence that he had over the animals of the Tiny Island.

The Wise Cat knew that these two apex predators, with their pure and strong hearts and raw energy, could soon become joint rulers of the Tiny Island. Once Strong Lion overcame his recklessness and Clumsy Tiger her clumsiness, they would reign together, and nothing would be able to stop them.

The Wise Cat was scared the Capricorn might use black magic against his stepson and kill him if the union of the Lion and the Tigress continued.

What the Wise Cat did not know, however, was that the Capricorn already knew. He had sent the Black Falcon to follow his stepson secretly because he had already had his suspicions for some time. Since Strong Lion had met Clumsy Tiger, he had spent most nights with her and not at the cave of his stepparents.

The Black Falcon brought the Capricorn the news about the Lion and the Tigress being a couple. The Capricorn did not like this at all. If Strong Lion had a true apex predator at his side, he would soon become the ruler of the Tiny Island.

Right now, all animals feared the Capricorn. But if the Lion rose to power, the influence that the Capricorn wielded over the other animals would vanish.

The Capricorn recognised the Tigress from the White Mountains, when he was still the Black Goat. He also remembered that she had not abandoned the Mountain Lion when he transformed into the White Wolf. With her determination and strength, she was a real threat to him.

The Capricorn understood that he had to fight the union of the Lion and the Tigress. He also knew that if their love for each other grew stronger, he would stand no chance. So he needed to come up quickly with a plan for how to separate the two lovers.

He recalled that he had only been able to drive a wedge between the Mountain Lion and the Tigress because of the Mountain Lion's greed. When the Mountain Lion transformed into the White Wolf, he had forgotten his most precious memory—that he loved his family.

Things were, however, more complicated with Strong Lion as he was not interested in hoarding diamonds. He simply wanted to lead a good life on the Tiny Island. But the Lion was prideful, and that would cause the downfall of the love between him and Clumsy Tiger.

On the same day he heard the news about the two being lovers, the Capricorn mixed two potions of highly sophisticated black magic—one for Strong Lion and one for the Wise Cat. The two potions had different effects on the two animals.

As they had never trusted the Capricorn, they did not eat the food or drink the water that was kept in the cave. The Capricorn, therefore, secretly put the potion for Strong Lion into the waterhole near their cave, as he knew that the Lion would drink from it.

The magic potion changed the Lion's perception. He no longer regarded the Tigress as his equal. Instead, he saw her through a mirror of distortion as a vulnerable animal who had been weakened by her battles, who was needy and only a burden.

The Capricorn hoped that Strong Lion would become disloyal to the Tigress and would look for another female predator to mate with.

The Capricorn had mixed a different potion for the Wise Cat. Although she was guarded towards him, she did not see it coming. One day, the Capricorn managed to put the magic potion for the Wise Cat into some prey that Strong Lion had hunted for her.

The potion fuelled her jealousy towards Clumsy Tiger, which she had so far carefully hidden. The Wise Cat well understood that the Tigress had a strength that went beyond the usual strength of an apex predator because of what she had been through in her animal life. The potion spurred her fear that Strong Lion would move away from her and into the cave of the Tigress and that she would lose the intense connection with her stepson.

CHAPTER SIX

The Final Separation

The next time Strong Lion saw Clumsy Tiger, he perceived her completely differently. He took her kindness as weakness and her good heart as foolishness.

Day after day, he picked something else that he could argue about with the Tigress.

One time he told her that it was her fault that a group of hyenas looked at her with admiration because she was so beautiful. He claimed that her fur was too shiny that day.

Another time he was jealous that the Tigress ran long distances with the Grey Wolf to enhance her strength and agility so that she could hunt more efficiently on the Tiny Island.

'I can also train you to run faster, and I have more endurance than the Grey Wolf. Why do you need his help?' the Lion complained angrily.

Yet another time he was annoyed simply about being asked to help the Tigress train Cub Leo how to hunt like a lion. Clumsy Tiger said to Strong Lion that he could show the lion cub how to hunt in the savannah much better than she could.

Strong Lion accused Clumsy Tiger of having developed an attitude because she wanted him to help her with so many things.

'You are the neediest animal I have ever met,' he told her on that occasion.

Strong Lion had a lot of things going on in his life and wanted to make the leap to the next level. Although he was still young and inexperienced, he wished that he would soon become the ruler of the Tiny Island.

He wanted the Tigress to understand this, but she ignored his desire for greatness and simply murmured that he would be fine and that he still had time to rise to power.

The Lion felt as if he was not being taken seriously by the Tigress as she ignored his aspirations. As a result, they started roaring at each other even more often.

One day, the Tigress discovered that something wonderful yet unexpected had happened. Clumsy Tiger could feel that she was carrying cubs under her heart. She was joyful and pleased and expected Strong Lion to feel the same way.

But he thought that he was not ready to have his own cubs, as he was just preparing for a new adventure. He also secretly believed that it would be inappropriate for the future ruler of the Tiny Island to have cubs with the Tigress.

Clumsy Tiger felt disheartened by his cold behaviour, and she started roaring at him even more frequently.

Strong Lion felt disrespected because she would not understand that all he craved from her was respect for his nature and character.

Later, an event occurred that Strong Lion had a hard time coping with. While they were spending a beautiful romantic evening together at a secluded waterhole, Clumsy Tiger recalled a time when she had talked to the White Horse at the waterhole. Whether imagined or not, Strong Lion saw a smile on her face as she recalled the memory. He was enraged.

'How can you smile? Do you not love and respect me?' he roared at the Tigress.

'I honestly do not understand your jealousy. I have no romantic feelings for the White Horse, and we are just friends. There is absolutely no point in making such a fuss about the meeting,' the Tigress replied.

But Strong Lion was deeply hurt because he was jealous by nature. He showed the Tigress his discontent by turning cold. As they were both stubborn creatures, they roared at each other and had an epic fight.

Clumsy Tiger felt rejected by the Lion. She had his unborn cubs under her heart and was disheartened by his aggression towards her.

Strong Lion felt disrespected by the Tigress because of the White Horse and her fond memory of their conversation. That night, the Lion stormed off and left Clumsy Tiger alone at the waterhole. He retreated to his cave, and the Tigress took it very badly.

Meanwhile, the Wise Cat, furious in her jealousy towards Clumsy Tiger, tried to convince the Lion that the Tigress was no match for him and suggested that they should go their separate ways.

After the incident at the waterhole, Strong Lion did not visit the Tigress for some time. However, they met by chance at a little waterhole. Strong Lion still acted cold and told the Tigress that he wanted to go to another small island for a couple of days on his own.

Clumsy Tiger was enraged. How could he even think of going without her? This time, the Tigress stormed off and left the baffled Lion behind at the waterhole.

Back in her cave, Clumsy Tiger decided that she could no longer deal with him being so cold. As she had an impulsive nature, she took her cub and went to the Outer Islands, which were not far from the Tiny Island, for some days. She informed the Lion about her departure with only a quick roar from a distance.

Now it was the Lion's turn to be utterly mad at Clumsy Tiger. How could she simply vanish without reconciling with him first? He felt that she was being ungrateful to him after he had put so much effort into healing her wounds.

What he could not know was that the Tigress had felt the immediate urge to retreat as she did not want more stress and roaring with Strong Lion. She was concerned about the unborn cubs under her heart.

And she could no longer bear the fact that Cub Leo never left the cave, lying around lazily the whole day and roaring at the Tigress that she should hunt for him, instead of hunting for himself.

Clumsy Tiger had taken off to the Outer Islands with Cub Leo to put some distance between her and the Lion in the hope that they would both calm down.

But things did not turn out well. Instead of acknowledging that she needed some space for herself, Strong Lion decided that enough was enough and that he could no longer deal with her attitude. Upon her return from the island, he at first ignored her and then finally visited the Tigress in her cave.

Clumsy Tiger was happy to see Strong Lion, but he told her that he was leaving her to look for a lioness. In his rage, he even bit Clumsy Tiger on her neck, claiming that it was her fault that she was not a lioness. The Tigress was bleeding from the Lion's bite and a slow, thin, constant thread of blood ran down her neck. Strong Lion stormed off after he told the Tigress that she was no longer his mate.

When he visited her a few days later to make sure that she was alright, the Tigress carefully covered the wound with leaves so that the Lion could not see it. So he perceived her to be as beautiful and strong as ever.

But Clumsy Tiger was deeply hurt. The wound in her neck had stopped bleeding, but the wound in her heart continued to bleed. Also, her old scar, which had almost healed, was hurting again.

Clumsy Tiger did not understand why Strong Lion had left her. She also did not know why he had changed his mind so quickly.

She retreated to her cave and decided that she would never again speak to the Lion. Clumsy Tiger lost his unborn cubs on the same night—maybe because her heart was broken, but more likely because her destiny was something else.

CHAPTER SEVEN

The Fierce Tigress

One day, the Red Fody, a friend of the Tigress, visited her. Clumsy Tiger fondly recollected how the Golden Watersnake had wrapped herself around her paw and that of the Lion and forged their spiritual bond.

'This has to stop now! You cannot for ever linger in old memories of Strong Lion. You have to move on; you have to move forward; you have to grow,' the Fody chirped.

She was angry that the Tigress was reminiscing about the Lion instead of fully settling on the Tiny Island, enhancing her skills to hunt in the savannah and developing her animal spirit.

Clumsy Tiger knew deep inside that the Fody was right.

She somehow even felt that Strong Lion had made the right decision in leaving her. Only his departure would allow her to grow and fully heal her heart from the loss of the Mountain Lion.

'Do you remember that we talked about the magic of the Underwater Waterfall some time ago? The Capricorn, who arrived on the Tiny Island as the Black Goat, was able to transform his animal spirit only because he dared to jump into the waterfall. Maybe a transformation would help you to heal not only the past hurts that are deeply ingrained in your spirit but also your current heartbreak,' the Fody suggested.

'You are so right! I no longer want to be Clumsy Tiger. That is the name that Strong Lion gave me, and whenever an animal calls me "Clumsy Tiger", it reminds me of him. I need to transform into another animal. And hopefully, the spiritual bond between Strong Lion and me will also perish in the process,' the Tigress replied. She had already experienced so much pain in her life that she acknowledged that only change could help her to recover.

The next day, the Tigress made her way to the Underwater Waterfall. In a leap of faith, she jumped into the ocean. She hoped that the transformation would heal her wounded heart, and she wished that she would no longer be Clumsy Tiger.

While diving into the waterfall, she hoped that she would become a lioness, as she still loved the Lion so much. She also remembered how strong she had been when she lived in the Asantian rainforest.

After a water vortex sucked her to the ocean floor, she quickly swam up from the bottom of the sea and reached the beach. She had not only survived, but she felt rejuvenated and invincible.

When she looked at her reflection in the water, she was utterly surprised that her mirror image was not that of a lioness. Instead, the water surface revealed a strong and determined Tigress.

The Tigress thought that she must not have been

ready to transform into a new animal yet. She realised, however, that her body was more muscular, her will more determined and her mind clear and strong. But also the warmth of her heart was gone. She was no longer Clumsy Tiger. The Fierce Tigress was born.

The Fierce Tigress raced back to her cave. The other animals were scared. She was no longer the Clumsy Tiger they knew and respected, a gentle Tigress who hunted only to still her hunger.

The Fierce Tigress was a killing machine. She hunted without mercy anything that came into her path, and she would not shy away from a fight. A pack of hyenas who thought they could take her down as a group fell prey to her.

The Fierce Tigress also treated her cub with less leniency and was unforgiving of herself. She would certainly have continued to become even more unforgiving if Cub Leo had not saved her heart.

After some time apart from the Lion, Leo said one sentence that broke down her defences: 'Strong Lion has left us.'

That was the moment she realised how much her cub was suffering, as he had looked up to the Lion. This insight changed her heart instantly. She took Leo in her paws and told him that she loved him, hugged and kissed him, and asked him for forgiveness.

That night something transforming happened. The Fierce Tigress woke up after midnight, and all of a sudden, her mind was flooded with fond memories of past times with Strong Lion. She understood better now where she had failed him and where he had failed her, and her heart was full of gratitude towards him.

The Tigress accepted that his departure had been necessary so that she could become stronger and wiser. She believed that he expected nothing less from her than to heal on her own.

The Tigress meditated; she pleaded to the animal spirits of her forefathers to forgive her for her pride and impatience and to fill her heart with meekness and gratitude.

CHAPTER EIGHT

A Step Beyond

After three days and nights of meditation, the Fierce Tigress had an epiphany. She understood that she had to transform her spirit again. The Tigress knew that no animal had survived the jump twice, but she was convinced that she could be reborn.

The Red Fody encouraged her to take the risk. So the Tigress went to the Underwater Waterfall and jumped in without thinking twice.

Clumsy Tiger was no more, the Fierce Tigress was no more, and a new creature was born: the White Tigress. Her fur had transformed from orange to white, and she had become a creature of legends.

She felt the Lion's spiritual presence intensely while changing her animal spirit. At the same time, she sensed that he, too, was levelling up. Although he was still young, he would soon be wise enough to become the new ruler of the Tiny Island. She felt happy for him but was also content that she was now the White Tigress.

During the following summer, the Tigress met several animals who guided her along her newly found path. Her mood was lightened by the White Cheetah, who also lived alone with her cub. In the Cheetah, the

Tigress had found a female predator with whom she could go hunting.

The Tigress met the Brown Bear, who admired her. They became friends and shared a passion for underwater walks. The Wise Cat had developed magic devices that made it possible for land animals to dive into the ocean and experience the colourful underwater world. Some brave predators, like the Cheetah, the Bear and the Tigress, enjoyed this kind of adventure.

The Brown Bear also dreamt of bringing flying balloons to the Tiny Island. He was a skilful and creative inventor of exciting new things that were appreciated by many animals.

The Tigress met the Proud Peafowl, with whom she started singing. She even gave her first singing performance in front of numerous animals.

And she also came across the Big Panda. He was incredibly strong but also wise and measured. The Tigress trained with him to increase her strength.

She was happy that she was no longer lonely because she had found new friends who showed her the beauty of the island.

Once the Tigress had made the decision to settle down on the Tiny Island, her heart calmed. Although she still missed Strong Lion, she coped well with her day-to-day life. She focused on hunting independently and her spiritual path.

The White Cheetah explained to her that life as a lone Tigress was not that bad, that she should concentrate on her cub and get on with her life—not think about the Lion.

The Red Fody, who was now coupled with the Giant Eagle, continued to meditate with her. She opened her animal spirit to a path beyond what the eyes can see. But the Tigress continued to think about Strong Lion, and she felt miserable when she heard his roar in the distance.

One day, however, changed her fate. The Tigress was unhappy and could not stop thinking about the Lion. As she had strained her shoulder badly while training with the Big Panda, she went to see the Healing Snake, who was another healer on the Tiny Island. He could cure an animal by giving them a tiny dose of his poison.

Even if some smaller animals were afraid of the Healing Snake, the predators liked to go to him as he could heal them quickly. He had a cave that he shared with the Wise Owl, which was near a small hill in the North of the Tiny Island. The Wise Owl was a hypnotist but also gave the animals advice on dealing with the fights among them.

When the Tigress arrived at the Healing Snake's cave, others were already waiting. She had to sit patiently until it was her turn.

The Tigress was well known on the island for her strength. The other animals did not know whether to fear or admire her. Most did both. It was murmured among them that the White Tigress no longer hunted for prey on land but instead had decided to catch fish to spare the mammals. But no one knew for sure.

When she entered the cave, the other animals whispered among themselves. Some greeted her respectfully; others were intimidated and ignored her.

Then the room fell silent. The atmosphere changed when the Black Panther entered. Most animals were scared. But the Panther sat down silently at the end of the line, behind the Tigress, and looked down.

The Tigress was lost in her own thoughts and did not look up, nor did she acknowledge the Black Panther. She was daydreaming of Strong Lion and how they had hunted together.

Finally, she looked up and her eyes met the eyes of the Panther. He smiled at her briefly but did not say anything.

The Tigress had immediately felt an intense tingle running down her spine when she looked into his deep blue eyes. It was as if she was looking into his animal spirit. She intuitively felt his pain—a lot of pain and incredible loneliness.

But she also experienced something else at that moment. She felt hope—hope that she would one day meet another predator and enjoy this world as a couple instead of being alone with Leo; hope that she would forget about Strong Lion and have only fond memories of him, not the longing that pierced her heart.

The Panther and the Tigress exchanged a few words. Then she was called into the inner cave of the Healing Snake. The Tigress gave the Panther a quick nod and went in.

The next day the Tigress went to see the White Cheetah, who instantly sensed that something had changed, as the Tigress was glowing and beaming with confidence.

'What happened?' the Cheetah asked.

'I saw the Black Panther, and he had such beautiful blue eyes. I felt hope again that my luck will turn one day,' the Tigress burst out.

The Cheetah laughed her unique cheetah laugh and did not say much. But she thought that the Tigress would soon be cured of her heartbreak.

Although the White Tigress looked out in secret for the Panther over the next couple of days, she did not see him. He had vanished like a ghost.

CHAPTER NINE

A Fight to the Death

One day, the Red Fody told the White Tigress a horrific story. The animals had become frightened to go to the only big lake on the Tiny Island, which was called the Great Waterhole.

A malicious Black Panther and his friends were roaming its shores and were killing every animal who came close to the lake. The Panther was often accompanied by other predators, including the aggressive Desert Leopard, the enormous Black Jaguar, the Snow Leopard and the Yellow Cheetah.

None of the animals who knew about the dangerous predators roaming around the lake dared approach the Great Waterhole. Not even Strong Lion was seen there.

The lake was the primary water source for many animals living in the centre of the island. At present, most of them were resorting to drinking the water from little springs and waterfalls. This water was, however, becoming scarcer by the day as it was summertime.

The White Tigress decided that something had to be done. Someone had to persuade the Black Panther to grant access to the Great Waterhole again.

'He will simply kill you. He will not listen to you; you have no chance,' the Fody warned the Tigress, who had no doubt whatsoever that she would be able to either convince the Panther or beat him in a fight.

Even though she listened to the Fody more often than not, she was also incredibly stubborn. If the Tigress was certain of something, there was no holding her back. And she was confident that she had to take action.

The Tigress left Young Leo with the White Cheetah and travelled the great distance from the Cheetah's cave in the North to the Great Waterhole. She was exhausted when she reached her destination, so she decided to rest close to the lake for the night, assuming that she would either speak with or fight the Panther the next morning.

What she did not sense was that she was being watched. The Yellow Cheetah had reported to the Black Panther that a large predator was swiftly approaching the Great Waterhole.

A group of bats, who were also under the Panther's command, had brought the news to him that she was resting not far from the lake.

As he enjoyed measuring his strength against other predators, the Panther went alone to the place where the Tigress was sleeping. He reached the spot shortly after sunset.

Even though he was as quiet as possible, the Tigress sensed the smell of another predator and woke up. She pretended that she was asleep so that he would come closer.

With a leap, the Panther charged the Tigress. His intention was to kill her with one bite directly to her throat.

Although he was incredibly swift, she rolled away at the last second and stood on her paws, ready to fight him.

The Black Panther hesitated as he could not entirely see the animal opposite him. However, he realised that her smell was strangely familiar to him.

'What do you want here?' he roared. 'This is forbidden territory!'

The Tigress, who was usually swift with her words, was speechless for a second.

'The Great Waterhole belongs to all animals of the Tiny Island. Many of them are suffering thirst because you are denying them access!' she finally roared back.

'You do not know what you are talking about. I cannot let anyone pass near the lake. The animals should go somewhere else to get water. It is our territory, and we will defend it,' he replied and shook his head in disbelief.

The Panther had recognised that the animal opposite him was the White Tigress, whom he had met some time ago.

'Go away, Tigress, and let me take care of my business around the Great Waterhole. The lake is protected by us now; no one is allowed to access it. You simply do not understand,' he roared as he was hesitant to fight her. He wanted to explain the reason to her, but before he could do so, the Tigress took action.

'I will reclaim the Great Waterhole from you!' she shouted angrily and jumped directly onto the Panther, catching him off-guard. He tumbled, but he rolled aside and stood strong the next moment, pushing her aside with his massive head.

The Tigress lost her balance, stumbled and fell onto the soft grass. There she lay as she saw the Panther's head bowed over her. Her last thought was that he would now bite her in the neck and that she would perish. She slowly lifted her head and looked him proudly in the eye, waiting for her defeat to happen. Then she fell unconscious.

When the Tigress woke up again, she found herself lying in a cave. She could barely move; she was too weak even to lift her head. Her eyes slowly adapted to the dim light, and she began to take in her surroundings.

The cave was dark and narrow and seemed to have been dug into the ground. It smelled muddy, like wet soil. Only a small amount of light came into the cave, from a source far away. I must be in a cave close to the Great Waterhole, she thought, before she dived into unconsciousness again.

The days and the nights passed. The Tigress had short periods when she was half-awake, interspersed with long periods of unconsciousness. Sometimes she saw blurrily the head of the Panther leaning over her and dripping water into her dry mouth.

Even though she could not think much, as her head was all fuzzy, she realised that she must be extremely sick, because she could not move at all.

One day, she finally woke up fully. When she opened her beautiful green eyes, the Black Panther was close to her. She looked into his eyes and saw the worry there. She instinctively knew that it was concern for her poor health. He was not there to attack her; he had helped her. She bowed her head slightly to thank him for his care.

'Do not move, you are still weak,' he said in a voice that was soft and warm, not sharp as she had heard it the last time, when they stood opposite each other, ready to fight to the death.

'You are strong, but you are lucky to have survived.

You are so stubborn, and you do not listen at all,' he chided.

If the Tigress had been more awake and attentive, she would have seen the amusement in his eyes. Instead, she became defensive and wanted to tell him that she was neither stubborn nor ignorant and that she could take good care of herself. She attempted to stand but failed miserably. She had to acknowledge that the Panther was right that she was still too weak to move.

Again their eyes met. She could see the generosity and the care in them. Once more, she felt the same way she had felt at their first encounter. It was as if she could see into his animal spirit. Although his blue eyes were incredibly beautiful, she could still see the pain, reflecting past suffering and sorrows.

It was as if the Panther had seen the pain of the whole world and had stored it in his eyes. She sensed that the suffering the Panther had experienced was far greater than hers. Now it fell to her to give him a smile to show him her compassion and at the same time her gratitude.

This time their eyes not only met but locked and did not want to unlock again. A light electrical current stroked the Tigress as it moved through her body.

This was not only the glimmer of hope that she had experienced when she first met him; there was something more—a feeling that she could not explain and that she had almost forgotten.

And this emotion was mixed with a sensation of peace and serenity. The Tigress shook herself lightly, almost as if she wanted to wake up from a dream.

At the same moment, the Panther looked away, obviously feeling uneasy that he had let his deep care for the Tigress shine through.

He took charge again and began to explain to her what had happened, as he could sense that she wanted to know why she had been so sick.

'When you came near the Great Waterhole and lay down to rest, you got infected with the Black Plague. It quickly made you weak, and when you wanted to fight me, you simply stumbled and fell unconscious. Most animals die within a few days once they have contracted the disease,' he said and again looked sorrowful. At that moment, the strong Black Panther appeared almost fragile and helpless.

The Tigress understood all of a sudden.

'That is why you kill all the animals who come close to the lake. You do not want the whole island to get infected,' she murmured, still wondering how she could have caught the Plague by simply lying in the grass.

The Panther guessed her thoughts.

'The Black Plague is dangerous and can spread easily. It is something we have not seen on this island before. There are many rodents who live around the lake. They all carry it but do not die from it. Wherever they poop, the Plague can spread. And they poop a lot on the grass around the lake,' he explained and smiled as he could see that the Tigress was amused at the thought.

'Although the Plague is killed by the sunlight, the rodents are active during the night, and this is when

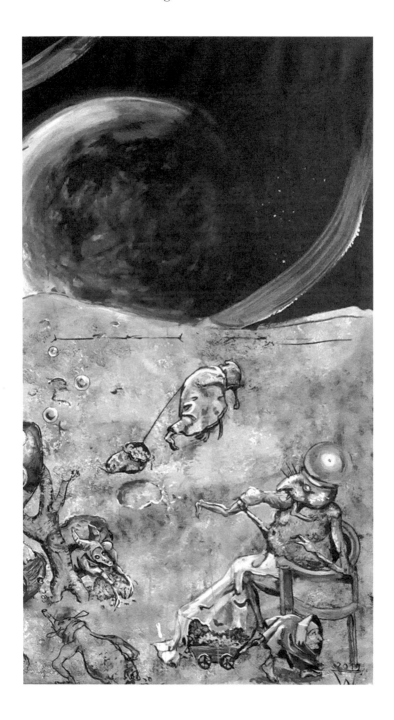

they spread the disease around the Great Waterhole. They are numerous, and they live underground, so we cannot find and kill them all. However, they stay close to their holes by the lake and do not move very far. Otherwise, we would already have a depopulated Tiny Island,' he added.

'So there is no cure?' the Tigress demanded to know.

'Unfortunately not, nothing at all. Almost all animals die from it, but luckily you survived,' the Panther responded. Now he almost smiled, and she could sense the relief in his voice.

'But I almost did not make it. You cared for me the whole time and made sure that I got water and recovered,' she acknowledged gratefully.

'You are a strong predator. I was confident that you had a chance, so I carried you to my cave and let you rest until you healed,' he said.

The Black Panther could see that she was deeply moved by his selflessness.

Within a few days, the Tigress had fully recovered. She started to like the Panther very much because he was so caring towards her. Every time she looked for a moment too long into his bright blue eyes, she had butterflies in her stomach.

She did not know how he felt but realised that he was attentive and friendly, albeit shy and polite. She, however, always saw the deep sadness and torment in his eyes. It was as if she almost experienced his pain physically.

One day, she felt strong enough to go back to the Cheetah's cave and be reunited with Young Leo.

'I will go home today,' she said to the Panther. 'I am healed, and I need to see Leo.'

The Black Panther shook his head, which made the Tigress uneasy.

'You cannot go now!' he replied, raising his soft voice. 'It is already too late. You would have to cross the infected area during the night, and you might spread the Plague. I am afraid that you will need to wait until tomorrow morning, once the sun is shining on the grass around the lake.'

'I understand. But then please tell me your story while we are waiting together for the sunrise. I always see the sadness in your eyes. I recognised it the first time we met at the Healing Snake's cave,' the Tigress responded.

The Panther was an equally good observer and replied, 'I can also see the pain in your eyes. I share my story with only a few animals, but I am happy to share it with you, as you seem to have suffered incredibly, too.

'But one thing—please do not judge me. I have always wanted to do good things, but while fighting for the good, I have sometimes lost my path, and I have done terrible things to cruel animals because I thought they deserved it. I was wrong in so many respects when I did not show mercy to those who did wrong to the weak and helpless. Out of anger, I found them, and I made them suffer for the suffering that they had caused to others.'

'I understand,' the Tigress said, 'but sometimes we have to rise above our anger and forgive those who cannot be forgiven. I am happy to listen to your story, and I will also tell you mine.'

They exchanged a deep look of trust, and both instantly knew that whatever they shared would stay between them. The Tigress told the Panther her story. After she had finished, it was his turn.

CHAPTER TEN

The Story of the Black Panther

Once again the Tigress saw the sadness in the Panther's eyes when he began to tell his story. It was almost unbearable for her. She had to look away; otherwise, she would have burst into tears. Again she felt he was deeply torn inside his spirit.

'It is fine if you do not want to share your story. I do not judge animals because of their past. I see only their present actions. I understand the pain you must feel because you have to kill animals who approach the Great Waterhole as they have come into contact with the Plague,' the Tigress said and softly laid her paw on his.

'My past affects my present, as it shaped who I am today. I want you to know my past—at least a little bit. I cannot tell you the whole horrible truth, however. You have been through enough, and you know yourself what animals are capable of doing to each other,' the Black Panther replied. Then he started his story.

My parents lived in the Asantian rainforest. They enjoyed it there a lot. Before I was born, they made their way to Avaria. My father thought that he had to bring justice to the world. He had heard that

the current Lion King was terrorising the animals there. Many animals had already died during his tyrannical reign.

A group of Black Panthers from Asantia were sent to Avaria by the Silver Dragon. He paid them diamonds to fight and defeat the Lion King there.

My mother, who was carrying me under her heart, did not want to follow them, but she had no choice. Once my father had made up his mind, he was stubborn, and so she had to join him.

The Silver Dragon led the way. Although the journey was dangerous and burdensome, all the Black Panthers whom the Dragon had sworn in arrived safely with their families in Avaria.

The Black Panthers started their mission to fight the cruel Lion King and his followers while the Silver Dragon returned to Asantia. Although my father had been a healer in the Asantian rainforest, he became a warrior.

The Lion King had a Black Goat as his adviser who must have fogged his mind with magic.

At the start of his reign, the Lion King was just, but he turned violent after the Goat appeared and made him believe that the other animals wanted to steal the diamonds he had been hoarding for a long time. Many animals were killed by the Lion King and his followers.

When the Black Panthers from the Asantian rainforest arrived, things changed for the better, as they challenged him. After many fights, the tables turned in their favour.

Before they could kill the Lion King, he fled, together with his Lion Queen and their cub. Even a cruel ruler wants to protect his family.

The Lion King must have feared that my father and his friends would kill not only him but also his heir. He knew that the Black Panthers would not leave the cub alive as they would have created a powerful enemy.

The Lion King ran away with his family to the shores of Avaria, but the group followed them. The Lion King killed a donkey and put his body on a plank they had found on the shore. They had decided to flee together across the ocean.

They put the lion cub on the plank, but before they could set off, the Black Panthers arrived and attacked them. The Lion Queen pushed the plank into the ocean and decided to fight beside the Lion King. She did not want to flee like a coward. The Lion King and his Queen were both killed in the fight.

The Black Panthers showed no mercy to the Lion Queen as she had chosen to fight alongside the Lion King instead of fleeing with her cub. They did not bother following the cub, however, as he would surely die on the endless ocean.

'That must have been Strong Lion. I mean the cub must have been him. He made his way across the ocean to the Tiny Island, and by a twist of fate, was adopted by the Capricorn and the Wise Cat. Many animals claim that the Capricorn was the Black Goat before.

'Oh, what a fate for Strong Lion! He always instinctively mistrusted the Capricorn, and now I know why. The Goat was responsible for his father turning cruel and unjust because he used black magic on him,' the Tigress interrupted the Panther's story. Then she remembered that she wanted to listen and again fell silent.

'You know, Tigress,' the Black Panther continued, 'we animals are always responsible for our own fate. Black magic can harm us only if we have the seed of those actions that we take already inside us. It cannot harm us if our spirit is pure.'

The Tigress sighed and said, 'I know.' She looked sad as she thought of the Mountain Lion and the greed that had made him vulnerable to the magic of the Goat.

'Please continue with your story, Black Panther,' she added, so as to distract herself from her sad thoughts about the Mountain Lion.

After I had grown up, my father wanted me also to fight for justice. I did not want to at first, but he convinced me because the injustice in Avaria continued.

The cruel Lion King was followed by ten even crueller lions who had divided Avaria among themselves. They were the younger brothers of the Lion King, and they stepped in to reign after him. They were brutal predators, ruling through fear and injustice.

The Lion Brothers had many followers. They promised those who served them diamonds that other animals had to find for them in the Grey Mountains.

They did not respect the cubs of those animals either. Instead, they sent them into the Grey Mountains to find diamonds, even if it meant that they had to crawl inside the tiniest clefts. Many of those cubs died a horrible death.

The Lion Brothers also did not respect the females of the other predator species, like leopards, panthers and cheetahs. If these females did not submit to their orders and mate with them, they would kill them and their cubs.

Often, they killed other predators simply because they could do so. It seemed as if they found joy in disgracing and killing any animal who was weaker than them.

They had no mercy because they were out-and-out beasts. I think it might have been the magic of the Black Goat that made them become so cruel. But to be honest, they must already have had the beast inside them.

The Goat vanished shortly before my father and his friends caught and killed the Lion King. But as the Goat had already subjected the Lion Brothers to his magic, things only got worse.

When I reached maturity, I could hardly bear the injustice in Avaria. I saw those Lion Brothers and their followers indiscriminately killing weaker animals, in particular cubs and female predators, to keep all other animals in fear.

Although we initially numbered only a few

offspring of the original Black Panthers, our group of defenders grew continuously.

Many other predators, such as leopards and cheetahs, who had lost their females and cubs joined our fight against the Lion Brothers. But we were not strong enough yet.

Although we won more and more victories against them, we never captured even one of the Lion Brothers. They seemed to vanish whenever we came near to them. I think the Goat had given them some magic potions before he left so that we could never get hold of them.

It seemed that the fight against the evil would never end. The evil spread, and we could not control it. We grew frustrated and helpless.

Sometimes when I saw females and cubs disgraced and slaughtered, I was so sad that I wanted revenge. I could not forgive the Lion Brothers for what they had done.

I started going out alone, without my friends, to find a cruel lion or a hyena. Although I never encountered any of the lions, I found hyenas on most of those forays.

I did not ask many questions. I had to do something. So I substituted action and revenge for my sadness. I could not just be a bystander: it was my duty to bring balance to this world. That was what I had sworn to myself and my father.

The White Tigress looked into the Panther's sorrowful eyes. He had to have seen so many cruel things in his animal life that he could not help but become an executor. The Black Panther must have guessed her thoughts.

'I am not proud of what I have done, but if it had not been for my friends and me, Avaria would still be ruled by the cruel Lion Brothers,' he said.

'So how did the fight end, and why did you end up on the Tiny Island?' the Tigress asked.

The Lion Brothers would only go out in pairs, and they always surrounded themselves with many hyenas. At first, we were not able to get close to them, and they continued to kill the females and cubs of other predator species.

But our fate changed when the Silver Dragon sent us more warriors from other places. Among them was the Black Jaguar from a distant continent, the Desert Leopard, the Yellow Cheetah and the Snow Leopard. We were now many predators and finally stood a chance against the Lion Brothers and their followers.

One day, we found a female lion cub in the savannah. She was hidden in a hollow tree. Not far from the tree, her parents lay dead, as well as her younger brother.

She told us that two lions and many hyenas had come. They had requested the lion couple to follow them and give them their cubs to be trained as warriors in service of the Lion Brothers.

Her parents had refused. They were free-spirited lions who did not want to follow them.

As the female cub had been fearful, she had hidden in the hollow tree when she saw them coming. Her brother had not, and that decision had sealed his fate.

One lion had killed the male cub by unexpectedly biting him in his neck while talking to his father.

The parents had immediately attacked the two lions. They had stood no chance whatsoever as they were assaulted from behind by the hyenas while fighting the lions.

The female cub had seen everything from her hiding place. It must have torn her heart apart. She was not discovered and survived because the traumatic events silenced her.

We came along when her family had already been dead for a while. The cub must have sat inside the hollow tree the whole night. When we arrived in the morning, searching for the Lion Brothers, we saw the dead bodies.

We did not think that anyone could have survived, but the Yellow Cheetah found the cub.

I instructed the Yellow Cheetah to take the lion cub to our caves. We would care for her, and one day, she would get the chance to avenge her dead family.

Meanwhile, the Black Jaguar and I followed the lions' tracks. We were able to surprise them during the night. They had started getting careless because they had never been caught before.

We killed the two Lion Brothers first and then took on the hyenas, who had tried to run away. I remembered the torment in the eyes of the lion cub, and I enjoyed killing those brutal predators slowly and mercilessly.

I was almost in a blood rage, and I remember having contradictory feelings that night.

First, I felt relief that I could bring balance to this world by killing those who had barbarously slaughtered the lion cub's parents and brother.

Then I felt immense sadness because I had not been able to prevent her family from being killed.

I also felt inner torment, as I understood that I had crossed a boundary that day. I had let my rage take over by killing those lions and hyenas extra slowly.

Since that particular night, I have not been able to show forgiveness. I knew that I had crossed the line between good and evil. I sensed that one day, I would have to forgive myself for doing so, but since that night, I have been torn inside my spirit.

We took good care of the lion cub, and when the Young Lioness grew up, she could finally avenge her parents by fighting the remaining Lion Brothers.

Our fate, however, changed when we hunted down the last two lions. They had kept some magic potions from the Black Goat, and they caused a big fire in the savannah before we could catch them. Numerous animals died in that fire. It spread quickly, and we had to retreat to the ocean shore.

Many animals grabbed planks and tree trunks that were lying on the beach, pushed them into the ocean and jumped onto them to avoid being burned alive.

We wanted to protect ourselves, hoping that we could float back to the shore once the fire had subsided. We were unlucky: a strong wind blew across the ocean and moved our planks quickly out to sea, so no turning back was possible.

Not only predators but other animals, too, made it to the planks. They were less lucky, because we had to eat them. There were also many rodents on the planks.

When my friends finally started eating the rodents, many of them became ill and died. We stopped eating them when we understood that they made us sick if we touched them. So we kept our distance. We did not even dare to throw them off the planks.

We finally made it to the shores of the Tiny Island. The strongest of us had survived.

Unfortunately, some of the rodents were also still alive and reached the shores. I believe they may be the same rodents who are now living at the lake and spreading the Black Plague.

However, I cannot imagine that those rodents made it to the Great Waterhole on their own. It seems almost as if someone placed them around the lake as they appeared only recently—many full moons after we arrived on the Tiny Island.

Regrettably, shortly before we reached the shore, we lost the Young Lioness, who was blown somewhere else by the wind. I hope that she survived, as I raised her as my own cub. I searched for her along the shore, but I could not find her.

The Black Panther had finished his story.

'I am sorry for your loss, but I am sure that the Young Lioness is still alive. Maybe she was rescued by someone and brought to their cave, where she is safe now,' the Tigress suggested.

Her thoughts wandered to memories of Strong Lion. She remembered how he had found her and had made sure that her wounds healed. Maybe he had rescued the Young Lioness. In her, he might also have found a lioness to mate with, she concluded. The Tigress did not share her thoughts with the Panther, though.

'I am sure that she was found. Do not worry, one day you will meet her again,' she simply said.

The Black Panther looked deep into her eyes, grateful that she had given him hope.

CHAPTER ELEVEN

A Goodbye

It was almost dawn when the Black Panther finished his story. The Tigress was deeply moved by it. Although she had already sensed what a brave and strong-willed predator he was, she had not been aware of the torment he had gone through. Even though he had endured so much suffering, he was kind and caring towards her.

The Tigress soon had to leave to meet Young Leo and the White Cheetah, who surely expected her to be dead.

She regretted leaving the Panther's cave as she felt comfortable in his presence. It had been a long time since she had felt that way. It was soothing for her spirit. For once, she did not have to take care of anyone else; instead, she was the one being cared for.

Sometimes the Tigress grew tired of being a fearless apex predator. She wished for nothing more than to have a companion by her side, someone who would defend her when needed so she could rest from the endless struggle for survival.

And there was the Black Panther. Even though he was not a tiger himself, he was as strong and fearless as the Tigress. When she looked into his blue eyes to say goodbye, she knew that she had fallen in love.

'I will run with you until you reach the border between the lake's surroundings and the savannah,' the Panther said swiftly, disturbing her thoughts. 'It is my turn to patrol around the Great Waterhole to make sure that no animal comes near the lake.'

The Tigress could see the sorrow in his eyes, reminding her that he would again have to kill any animal who came too close to the Great Waterhole.

She gave the Panther a tender stroke with her paw to show that she understood the sacrifice he was making for the safety of the Tiny Island.

Both left the cave swiftly. Just then, the sun rose above the lake. But they could watch it only for a moment before they had to continue. When they reached the savannah, they knew it was time to say goodbye.

The Tigress wondered whether she would see the Panther again.

'Goodbye,' he said.

'Goodbye,' the Tigress replied. 'I will never forget how much you have helped me. If you should ever need my help, you can count on me.'

'Thank you. I will remember that, but I hope I will not need it. It is good to have you as a new friend and not as an enemy,' he said.

'I was not your enemy. I only wanted to reclaim the Great Waterhole, and I truly overestimated my power to do so. Instead of winning a victory, I fell ill and nearly lost my life. Thank you for saving my life,' the Tigress added.

'It was not I who saved your life but your strong

animal spirit. I only gave you shelter, and anyone would have done that for the White Tigress. And thank you for sharing your story with me. I was truly moved,' the Panther remarked.

They looked into each other's eyes and felt so much love, but they said nothing. The Tigress turned her back without any further goodbye and ran across the savannah under the now burning sun.

If she had looked back even once, she would have seen that the Panther watched until she was out of sight.

The Tigress arrived at the Cheetah's cave when the sun was still high. Young Leo was full of joy to see his mother, and he jumped up and down.

Although the Cheetah had told him that his mother would come back, he had been petrified that she might not and feared becoming an orphan. The White Cheetah was also full of joy to see the Tigress alive. She almost wanted to jump up and down in the same way as Leo.

When Leo fell asleep that night, the Cheetah asked the White Tigress to tell her what had happened at the Great Waterhole. She had so many questions.

Why had the Tigress been away for so long? Had she been successful in convincing the Black Panther to grant access to the Great Waterhole to all animals?

While she listened to the Tigress recount her adventure, she simply nodded her head, smiled or giggled when the Tigress spoke about the Panther with such passion in her voice.

As she was a good listener, she let the Tigress speak. She intervened only once, when she did not understand why the Tigress had fallen like a stone in the soft grass while fighting the Panther. She was concerned when she learned about the Black Plague and asked many questions.

But the Tigress did not have all the answers. In particular, she was not sure how the rodents from the planks had made their way to the Great Waterhole. They both decided to talk to the Red Fody the next day to find out whether she knew more.

CHAPTER TWELVE

An Unexpected Meeting

The next morning, the Cheetah and the Tigress crossed the savannah in the North to find the Red Fody. They ran fast but steadily. Suddenly, they heard a cheerful roar from behind.

The Tigress immediately understood that it was Strong Lion. Although a little uncomfortable, the Tigress stopped and turned around.

She saw Strong Lion, prideful as ever, and beside him a Lioness who was pregnant. The Lion's eyes beamed with pride when he saw the Tigress looking at the slightly bulging belly of his mate.

'I am so happy for you. That is all you ever wanted—your own cubs and a beautiful lioness,' the Tigress said to Strong Lion.

'Yes,' he replied briefly, obviously remembering the cubs whom the Tigress had once had under her heart. Strong Lion attempted to continue on his way, but the Tigress smiled at him, knowing exactly his thoughts.

'Wait, please introduce your mate to me. To my knowledge, there has been no lioness on the Tiny Island until now,' the Tigress said. Then she turned her eyes to the Lioness, and remarked, 'I am the White

Tigress. I came on a plank to the Tiny Island with my cub. Strong Lion rescued me.'

'I am the Young Lioness. I was washed up on the shore as well, but I came from Avaria, not from the Asantian rainforest like you,' she burst out, relieved that the Tigress was not offended to see them.

Strong Lion looked apologetically at the Tigress. He had obviously spilled out her story to the Young Lioness, but the Tigress just smiled away his unease.

'That is very interesting. Not many animals make their way on a plank to the Tiny Island; you must have strength and endurance,' the Tigress observed. 'We are on our way to the Red Fody. I was at the Great Waterhole to find out why a group of predators is killing all animals who approach the lake. I have troublesome news that I want to discuss with her. If there is one animal who will know why a mysterious illness is spreading around the lake, it is the Fody,' the Tigress added, addressing both lions.

'You mean the Black Plague?' they replied at the same time.

Now the Tigress saw how much the Lioness admired Strong Lion. He must love that, she thought.

'You also know about the Black Plague? Please tell me all you know. It is important for us to find out why the Plague is spreading around the Great Waterhole,' she said to both of them. 'And, Young Lioness, please tell me all about your journey across the ocean.'

Although Strong Lion clearly wanted to start telling the Lioness' story, one look from the Tigress was enough to silence him. The Young Lioness began:

Avaria was ruled by ten cruel Lion Brothers. My parents and my brother were killed by two of them and several hyenas. I survived because I was hiding in a hollow tree where I used to play.

The next day, a group of predators came. They were following the two lions, but they arrived too late to save my family.

The Black Panther, who seemed to be the commander of those animals, looked at me with sorrowful eyes. When I told him who had killed my parents and how cruel they were, as if they had enjoyed killing them, he said to the Yellow Cheetah, 'Lead her to our caves and take good care of her. She is an orphan now. I will go with the Black Jaguar and hunt them down.'

Then they went off, and I went with the Yellow Cheetah to their caves. I was raised by them. When I was grown up, I became the Young Lioness and joined them in the fight against the Lion Brothers. Shortly before we had hunted down the last two Lion Brothers, they started a fire.

As the whole savannah burned—it was the dry season—we tried to rescue as many animals as possible and took them to the coast. When the fire finally reached the shore, numerous animals decided to flee certain death by grabbing planks and going into the water.

The wind was strong that day, and we drifted out into the ocean. Most animals did not survive on the planks because of the sun or white sharks, or simply because we were eating them. On the bigger planks, there were a lot of rodents.

My friends and I ate the tasty pigs first, and then we started killing the rodents. But we got ill, so we stopped eating them. Many of us died after eating the rodents, but some of us miraculously survived. Then, one day, when we thought everything was lost, we saw the shores of the Tiny Island and the wind was in our favour.

My plank drifted far away from my friends, and I landed on a different side of the island, where Strong Lion found me in the same way he found you.

The Tigress already knew the story from the Black Panther, but she had listened attentively. She understood better now how much predators such as the Young Lioness had suffered under the Lion Brothers and how important it had been that the Panther and his friends stop them.

She respected the Black Panther deeply for what he had done to protect the weaker animals, although she could never imagine herself fighting in such a manner.

The Tigress was utterly lost in her thoughts. Hearing the story of the Lioness, she remembered how she had woken up and looked into the eyes of Strong Lion.

When she caught herself having this thought, she had to lower her head, half ashamed at having such ideas in the presence of the new mate of Strong Lion. She respected the Young Lioness and knew from the story of her own cub what it meant to lose a parent.

The Cheetah noticed the Tigress lower her eyes, and she smiled at her compassionately. The Tigress knew that the Cheetah would laugh her loud cheetah laugh once they were alone and tease her about it.

'So, there were other predators with you? And the rodents were not all dead—some of them were still alive?' the Tigress asked, knowing the answer already.

'I do not know what happened to my friends. I have not seen them since,' the Lioness answered, looking a little sad.

'I have seen a cage with living rodents in the cave of Strong Lion's stepfather, the Capricorn, but I cannot imagine that they were the same rodents,' she added quickly, so as not to offend the Lion.

Now Strong Lion interrupted a little harshly: 'You never told me that!'

'I did not think it mattered,' she replied, looking at the Lion apologetically.

'Now I understand,' the Lion and the Tigress said at the same time.

'The Capricorn must have collected the rodents from the planks,' Strong Lion roared angrily.

'And some of the rodents he kept in the cage must have escaped,' the Young Lioness assisted.

'It is more likely that the Capricorn placed them around the Great Waterhole,' the Tigress opined.

'Very likely,' Strong Lion murmured.

When they looked into each other's eyes for a moment, they knew that it was certain.

'At least we know now who placed the rodents around the Great Waterhole so that the animals would come into contact with the Plague and die,' the Tigress explained.

'But why would the Capricorn do this?' the Young Lioness asked.

'Control, power, absolute control,' Strong Lion said, answering her question.

'He is a famous healer on the Tiny Island, but the animals do not trust him. If he were to find a cure for the Black Plague, all animals would worship him and make him the new ruler of the Tiny Island,' the Tigress continued the Lion's thoughts—just as she had always done when they were still together.

'That must be his plan. That is why he has been so friendly lately. He must be anticipating his final victory. But we must stop him before it is too late. We cannot have him rule the Tiny Island. It would be the end of justice and peace,' the Lion roared.

'So why has the disease not yet spread around the island?' the Young Lioness wanted to know.

'Because your friends from Avaria are hunting the rodents around the Great Waterhole. Those predators are immune to the Black Plague. They came into contact with the Plague when they were on the planks, but they survived the illness. Now they have to kill all animals who come close to the lake in order to prevent the Plague from spreading,' the White Tigress explained.

'But you went to the lake to stop them doing this, and they could not kill you because you were too strong and too fast,' Strong Lion said, looking proud that he could put together the whole story.

'Not quite,' the Tigress responded. She could see the disappointment in his eyes at being wrong for once.

'I did indeed want to challenge these predators who came from nowhere and started to kill all animals who approached the lake.

'But I, too, fell ill when I lay down in the grass to rest before confronting them. When I started to fight the leader of the group, I simply fell unconscious, but I was saved and cared for,' the Tigress said with a smile. She thought lovingly of the Panther who had cared for her in his cave.

'The Black Panther must have taken good care of you,' the Lioness guessed the Tigress' thoughts and laughed.

'He has a good heart, and I cannot imagine that he would have dared to kill such a beautiful Tigress as you,' she continued, smiling knowingly. Now the White Cheetah laughed a loud cheetah laugh, and all three females laughed together as if they were old friends, thoroughly breaking the ice between them.

Only the Lion stood a little aside, not knowing what to think, as he simply could not imagine that the Tigress might find another apex predator who equalled him.

'We will keep you informed, Strong Lion,' said the Tigress, remembering all of a sudden that they wanted to meet the Fody. 'And it was lovely to meet you, Young Lioness. Thank you for telling us your story. Now we know about the Capricorn's plan, we can decide what to do. And all the best for your cubs,' the Tigress said, looking at both of them.

The Cheetah and the Tigress started running across the savannah to reach the tree of the Red Fody before dawn. The lion couple looked after them for a long while.

When the Lioness said, 'What a strong Tigress. I somehow admire her,' the Lion remembered the exciting times he had shared with the Tigress for a moment and almost sighed.

But deep down he was happy that he was in calmer waters now and that his wishes were finally about to come true: the Young Lioness, his own cubs and soon also three coyotes to protect his little family.

CHAPTER THIRTEEN

The Plan

When the Tigress and the Cheetah arrived at the Fody's tree, they admired the silence of the place. The tree was in the savannah of the North, beside a tiny waterhole.

It was big and green, and it had the most beautiful red flowers blossoming in its crown, looking magical. The animals of the Tiny Island called it the Flame Tree because its red blossoms looked like flames.

The Tigress and the Cheetah knew that they would not be able to spot the Fody amidst the red crown unless she showed herself. Seemingly out of nowhere, she appeared and sat directly on the Tigress' left shoulder. The Tigress and the Cheetah sat under the Flame Tree and rested.

'You have beautiful yellow butterflies flying around your head,' the Fody addressed the Cheetah.

'I do not know where they come from. Everywhere I go, three yellow butterflies appear and then accompany me. This has been going on for a while. I love these butterflies, but I do not know why they are attracted to my head,' the White Cheetah said and laughed her beautiful cheetah laugh.

'They are your ancestors,' the Fody said, 'and they are flying around your head because they want to tell you that the one who is meant to be with you is near.'

'Really?' the Cheetah asked and looked doubtfully at the Fody.

Although the Cheetah was a beautiful predator who had a cub called Cham, she had not had a mate for some time. After the Grey Cheetah betrayed her, she did not want to have another male predator by her side and instead hunted on her own.

'Your future mate is near. He came only recently to the Tiny Island. When I tapped into the energy of the universe and your source energy, I felt that this predator would be the one who was made especially for you,' the Red Fody replied. Now the Cheetah was excited and decided to listen to the Fody carefully.

'Where does this predator come from? You know, I have lived my whole life on the Tiny Island, and I have never met another predator who serves my cub's needs and my own after the Grey Cheetah left us. And I am not as lucky as the Tigress, who met a predator who was made for her,' she said.

'Strong Lion was not made for her. He was not the right one. Although he is strong and intelligent and has a good heart, he is too prideful and was not committed enough to the Tigress as he wanted to find his lioness,' the Fody chirped angrily. She always looked gloomy when she talked about Strong Lion as she knew how much the Tigress had suffered when he had left her. She sensed that the Tigress had had lingering feelings for the Lion for a long time and wanted to make the point that she needed to forget him once and for all.

'And now he has finally found his mate,' the Fody added carefully so as not to hurt the Tigress.

The two female predators raised their heads simultaneously. The Red Fody was somewhat astonished that the Tigress seemed not to be surprised at all by the news.

'We know,' the Tigress said and told the Fody how they had met the lion couple.

'Yes, he seems to have had his wish fulfilled. And yours might finally have come true, too,' the Red Fody murmured.

'How do you know about the Black Panther?' the Tigress demanded to know, shocked that the Fody apparently knew everything already.

'She knows everything because she flies around the sky watching from high above and then gossips about the other animals,' the White Cheetah said laconically.

The Tigress knew that the Cheetah and the Fody were sometimes angry at each other, even though they were friends.

'Do not worry, Cheetah, I have not been able to gossip about you for a long time because you simply did not find a mate who was good enough for you,' the Fody replied, annoyed by the Cheetah's remark.

Now it was the Tigress' turn to laugh out loud, because the Red Fody no longer sounded like a wise oracle. When the Cheetah angrily turned her back on the Fody, offended and pretending that she had not heard the Fody's comment, the Tigress knew that she had to change the topic from mating and strong male predators.

'The Capricorn is likely behind the spreading of a serious disease around the Great Waterhole. They call it the Black Plague. It is lethal and also spreads easily.

We believe that the Capricorn must have released sick rodents at the shores of the lake, who then spread the disease.

'The Plague would already have infected the animal population across the Tiny Island if it were not for the Black Panther and his friends who arrived some time ago on the island. Unfortunately, they have to kill not only the rodents but also other animals who come too close to the lake. That is the only way that they can contain the Plague around the area of the Great Waterhole,' the Tigress explained.

'But they did not kill you! Come, tell me your story and all about this mysterious Black Panther,' the Fody insisted.

The Tigress told the Fody about the fight with the Panther, her illness and how he had taken good care of her.

'We need a plan to stop the Capricorn,' the Red Fody suggested after she had heard all about the Tigress' adventure.

'We are going to work out the plan tonight,' the Cheetah added. She agreed with what the Red Fody had to say for once.

It took the Tigress, the Cheetah and the Fody a while to develop a plan. It was a risky plan, but they hoped that it would work. They decided that they needed to capture the Capricorn.

They knew that the Capricorn was a threat to the entire Tiny Island and had to be stopped. Otherwise, he would spread the Black Plague across the island sooner or later, and many more animals would die.

'It is likely that the Capricorn must have found a cure for the Plague. Otherwise, he would not let the disease spread indiscriminately. Strong Lion believes that the Capricorn wants to use his knowledge of the cure to ascend to become the new ruler of the Tiny Island,' the Tigress explained. 'But we will need help. We cannot do this on our own. The Capricorn has many helpers to protect him, and poisonous snakes surround his cave,' she added.

'And the three elephants he has as a guard are truly frightening,' the Red Fody remarked.

'And we should not forget that he uses black magic,' the Cheetah commented.

'We need the Black Panther and his friends; otherwise, we have no chance whatsoever,' the Tigress said, now more determined than ever to stop the Capricorn.

'But can we trust the Panther at all? Who is to say that he and his friends will not betray us? Who can say that they will help us?' the Cheetah questioned the Tigress' suggestion.

'We have no other chance. We have to risk it. And I honestly think that we can trust the Panther. He could have killed me when I was sick, but he did not. He cared for me in his cave until I recovered,' the Tigress replied.

'You are in love. Your observation does not count because your judgement is clouded. But we will go together to the Great Waterhole and meet the Panther and his friends. I will then understand better whether they can be trusted,' the Cheetah said and laughed her unique cheetah laugh.

The White Cheetah was convinced about the strength of her judgement and her intuition. The Tigress decided not to argue with her suggestion. It would be best if they met the Panther and his friends together.

CHAPTER FOURTEEN

The Plan Falls Apart

While the Cheetah and the Tigress travelled the considerable distance to the Great Waterhole, the Red Fody decided that she would watch them from high above in the sky.

'I will call for help in case you need it,' she said and vanished into the red flowers of the Flame Tree.

The Tigress had hoped that they would meet the lion couple again while crossing the savannah so that they could help to catch the Capricorn, but they were nowhere to be seen.

Before dusk, they reached the shores of the Great Waterhole and approached the Panther's cave. But they did not get that far.

Before they reached the entrance, all hell broke loose. A huge black-spotted animal jumped on the White Cheetah and immobilised her in an instant. The Tigress could see that it was the gigantic Black Jaguar about whom the Panther had told her. The dying sun made it look as if his fur was on fire.

At the same time, the Tigress was charged by the yellow-spotted Desert Leopard and put down on the soil immediately. She was able to free herself, however, and stood in front of the Leopard.

'What are you doing? I am a friend of the Black

Panther. We have come here in peace to ask him for help. The Capricorn has to be stopped. He is trying to spread the Plague across the Tiny Island, and you will no longer be able to contain it to the area around the Great Waterhole. We need your help,' the Tigress roared.

When the Desert Leopard suddenly looked sad, she instinctively knew that something was wrong.

At the same moment, the Jaguar loosened the grip that he had on the Cheetah, although he was reluctant to do so. Then he turned his massive head to the Tigress.

'I am the Black Jaguar, and this is the Desert Leopard,' he introduced his yellow-spotted friend.

'The Black Panther vanished yesterday. We do not know where he is. Something must have happened. He was on patrol at the far end of the lake. The Desert Leopard and I were patrolling at the same time. We cover the area in such a way that we can just see the next patrol.

'He must have seen something suspicious in the savannah, for I saw him suddenly run off, but he did not come back to his cave before dusk. We searched for him the whole night, but he has vanished. I am glad that you have come. Maybe you can help us to find him?' the Jaguar said, looking worried.

The Tigress sensed that the Black Jaguar was in charge now the Panther had disappeared. She admired the fact the predators had organised their patrol so efficiently to prevent the Plague from spreading.

But she was also worried that the Black Panther

was gone. He had seemed so strong and determined that she could not imagine that another animal could overpower him.

For a moment, she wondered whether Strong Lion might have crossed his path and challenged him, considering his reckless nature. But then she calmed down, as she knew that the Lion was busy creating his own family.

She sensed that he was no longer the same reckless predator she had known but had become calmer and soon would become a responsible family father.

'Maybe the Black Panther was caught in some advanced trap. I doubt that any animal could charge him, as I have come to know him to be a fierce fighter,' the Tigress continued her thought process aloud so that everyone could hear it.

Suddenly, the Cheetah, who had been silent so far, gazing in admiration at the shining black fur of the Jaguar, interrupted the Tigress.

'I know of only one animal who could lay a trap that could capture an apex predator, and that is the Capricorn, who has not only black magic to assist him but also the hyenas and the giant elephants,' she said.

'Yes, you are right: only the Capricorn could have caught him. If we find the Capricorn, we are also likely to find the Panther, and then we can put an end to the threat that the Capricorn poses to the animals of the Tiny Island,' the Tigress added.

'That is a good plan,' the Jaguar responded a little absent-mindedly to the Tigress.

She noticed that the Black Jaguar had not looked

towards her while answering; he continued to stare at the beautiful White Cheetah, while the Cheetah stared back.

That is the predator who was made for her, the one the Fody mentioned, the Tigress thought and wanted to smile. She saw the Cheetah looking in admiration at the large, firm body of the Jaguar.

'You have to join us, with all your friends, to free the Black Panther,' the Tigress replied solemnly, addressing the Jaguar and the Leopard.

'That is not possible. Our friends have to continue to patrol around the Great Waterhole so that the Plague does not spread. But the Desert Leopard and I will accompany you so that we can find the Panther and apprehend the Capricorn,' the Jaguar replied abruptly as if he had been awoken from the spell cast over him by the Cheetah.

'Oh good! Nothing can happen to us if we are protected by your strength,' the Cheetah said—and the Tigress could see the relief in her eyes.

Now the White Tigress and the Desert Leopard both laughed aloud as they sensed the instant chemistry between the Cheetah and the Jaguar.

Without warning, the Jaguar suddenly started running towards the savannah, obviously slightly concerned that the mutual admiration between him and the Cheetah was so evident. The three other predators followed him swiftly, like shadows in the night.

CHAPTER FIFTEEN

The Rescue of the Black Panther

The cave of the Capricorn and the Wise Cat was not far from the Great Waterhole. The four predators reached it quickly, just after nightfall. The full moon was shining brightly, so they had to approach the heavily guarded cave carefully.

There was no way that they could get past the front entrance, which was guarded by three giant elephants and poisonous snakes.

'The Capricorn must be fearful for his life,' the Cheetah whispered.

'He may already know that we are planning something,' the Tigress added. 'When he captured the Black Panther, he would have realised that his friends would work out sooner or later what had happened.'

'I agree,' the Jaguar said. Although he did not want to show it, he was worried.

'Do you think he is still alive?' the Desert Leopard asked the Tigress.

'They need him. The Capricorn has to present a scapegoat to the other animals who does not come from the Tiny Island and claim that he spread the Black Plague.

'The cave has a back entrance. We need to try there. I hope that we will be able to rescue the Panther tonight,' the Tigress replied.

The four predators retreated from the front entrance and tried to approach the cave from the rear. The Tigress knew that the other entrance was impossible to find if one did not know where to search for it.

Luckily, Strong Lion had told the Tigress where the second entrance was when they had planned that she would visit him in secret, without the Capricorn knowing. That had never happened, but the Tigress still remembered the description the Lion had given her.

They would have to climb a hill, then cross a field of gravel and swim through a raging river to reach the back entrance.

Even though the route was easy for the Capricorn and the Wise Cat, as they could use their magic potions to aid them, it would be more difficult for the four predators as they were heavier and not used to climbing mountains or walking on stones.

But they were all determined. The Tigress because she wanted to rescue the one she loved. The Black Jaguar and the Desert Leopard because they wanted to save their friend and commander. The Cheetah because she was trying to help the Tigress—and maybe also because she wanted to stay close to the Jaguar.

The Tigress realised that she did not know the Cheetah as well as she had assumed. Although the Cheetah was trying to act unmoved in the presence of the Jaguar, the Tigress could see her admiring looks towards him when he was not looking.

On the other side, she could see how the Jaguar looked at the Cheetah with admiration. It seemed as if love had struck the two in a single moment.

When the predators reached the foot of the hill leading to the secret entrance to the cave, two paths opened up in front of them. The Tigress remembered that they needed to take the steeper trail.

'We need to take the right-hand path, which is steeper but will let us reach the rear entrance safely,' the Tigress said.

'I do not think so,' the Cheetah interrupted her. 'You must be mistaken. We should rather take the left-hand path because it seems to lead to the same cave and looks less dangerous.'

'I do not remember why, but Strong Lion said that I should take the trail on the right. He said that the left one would be more dangerous. I do not think that he would have misled me,' the Tigress insisted.

'Strong Lion simply wanted to impress you by implying that he always followed the harder path. Or he wanted you to put in more effort to see him,' the Cheetah responded and laughed her beautiful cheetah laugh.

'I think the Cheetah may be right. It is night, so the less steep trail would seem to be the safer option,' the Jaguar intervened as he wanted to agree with the Cheetah rather than the Tigress to show his appreciation for the Cheetah's wisdom.

Further, with his incredible weight, he was a little uncomfortable climbing up the steeper trail because he did not want to slip in front of the Cheetah. So he stormed ahead on the left track, followed by the Leopard and the Cheetah.

The Tigress hesitated for a moment. Strong Lion had not suggested the steeper path for nothing. She was convinced that they should take the right-hand track and not the left.

The four predators had almost reached the top of the hill when the Desert Leopard roared loudly. Although the Tigress could not see much, because a cloud covered the moon, she understood that something was wrong.

The Jaguar, who had taken the lead, had jumped over a shallow hole with ease. But the Leopard, who was directly behind him, had stepped into the hole.

When the Jaguar heard the Leopard's cry of pain, he went back and saw that the Leopard had been bitten by a large poisonous snake. Swiftly, he dragged his injured friend away and bit the snake in two. Then he took the Leopard on his broad shoulders and roared to the Tigress and the Cheetah that they should go back down the hill.

Once he reached the bottom of the hill, the Jaguar immediately bit into the wound where the snake had injected her poison, sucked and spat it out. The Leopard looked at him in gratitude, for he knew that the Jaguar had saved his life.

The four predators waited until sunrise as the Leopard was too weak to run and they did not want to risk the poison circulating throughout his body. Then they retreated to a little oasis in the savannah and spent the day there so that he had time to recover. The rescue of the Black Panther would have to wait until the next night.

The Tigress was angry with the Cheetah, who had not followed her recollection, but she did not say anything. The Cheetah was angry with herself for questioning the Tigress' memory. The Jaguar was angry with the Panther because he had run off into the savannah without him. And the Leopard was furious as it was he who had been bitten by the snake. So everyone was angry, but no one said anything.

The four predators waited patiently until the next sunset so they could make a second attempt to rescue the Panther. As night began to fall, the predators made their way to the hill. This time, no one questioned the recollection of the Tigress to follow the right-hand path.

Although the Jaguar was heavy, he climbed the path with relative ease as he was used to climbing trees. The Cheetah had no problems following the Jaguar on the steep trail as love gave her wings. The Leopard was reasonably recovered, although he could not match the speed of the others.

Only the Tigress struggled, as she was no longer used to climbing mountains. But she did not show it, because she was determined to rescue her beloved Panther. When they had reached the peak of the hill without encountering any snakes, they had to cross a gravel field, and the gravel pierced the paws of the predators. But again, no one complained.

After this challenge, they needed to cross a river. Although the Tigress and the male predators had no problems as they were good swimmers, the Cheetah struggled because she was relatively light. But the Jaguar and the Tigress took her between them so that she would not be carried away by the raging waters. They all made it safely across the river but had to rest for a while to recover their energy.

Because of their rescue mission, the predators had not hunted for the past two nights, apart from a small pig the Black Jaguar had caught at the oasis.

They were all hungry after climbing the path, walking through the gravel field and crossing the river. But they did not have time to stop for a hunt.

The Leopard had been lucky enough to catch a water rat while crossing the river. There was no point in sharing the rat as she was relatively small. Still, the Leopard ate only one half and pushed the other half towards the Tigress and the Cheetah. They shared the half rat, grateful to have at least something in their stomachs. The Leopard knew that the Jaguar would refuse to eat part of the rat and would want the two females to have it, so he avoided offering him any.

After the short rest, the four predators continued along the path, which led directly to the cave. The bright moonlight showed the way.

The Tigress knew that hyenas protected the long tunnel leading to the cave and that they would howl if they heard even the slightest noise. They would have to approach the back entrance in dead silence. The Tigress told the others that the beginning of the tunnel leading to the cave was to be found under a big Flame Tree.

'We also have to be careful of the poisonous snakes who hide in the tree. We cannot risk another snake bite,' the Tigress said, trying not to look at the Cheetah as she was still angry with her.

'Do not fear, Tigress,' the Jaguar said, 'I will approach the tree first and bite the heads off any snakes and kill the hyenas.'

The Black Jaguar noticed with satisfaction that the Cheetah was looking at him with respect.

The Tigress could see that he simply wanted to impress the Cheetah, and she smiled. It was a happy moment for her to watch those two predators who had fallen in love, and she was amused at how the Jaguar wanted to prove to the Cheetah that he was the ultimate apex predator. It reminded her a little of Strong Lion and his recklessness.

She was happy that she was in love with the Black Panther, who was more strategic. But then she remembered that the Capricorn had captured him. Even such a prudent animal as the Panther can be caught, the Tigress thought.

'Let us move—and be quiet,' the Jaguar commanded, and the others followed.

At the Flame Tree, the Tigress and the Cheetah witnessed how the two male predators were fast, silent killers.

In an instant, the Jaguar jumped into the tree and bit off the heads of two green snakes. The Tigress was impressed that he could see them at all, as the tree was green all the way up.

At the same time, the Leopard had torn apart a large tree python. Suddenly, the Jaguar jumped down from the Flame Tree directly onto the head of a highly venomous brown snake. The snake had almost reached the Cheetah, who had remained on the ground, watching the male predators killing the snakes.

'Hopefully, that is all the snakes,' the Tigress whispered to the Cheetah, who was frozen in fear because the snake had almost bitten her.

'Let us move quickly and silently before we encounter any more of them,' the Jaguar commanded.

They all knew that now the most challenging part of their adventure would begin. They had to find and climb through the tunnel leading to the cave entrance, where the hyenas would be waiting, ready to howl if they noticed the faintest unfamiliar sound or movement.

It took them a while to find the tunnel, even though the Tigress remembered that it was close to the tree root.

Eventually, they found it hidden in the dense undergrowth. They removed the undergrowth slowly and silently so that the hyenas would not hear them. Then everything happened quickly.

Without warning, the Jaguar jumped into the narrow tunnel leading to the cave, followed by the Leopard. The Tigress and the Cheetah heard only a faint howl. Then everything went silent.

The Desert Leopard came out of the tunnel.

'All clear. You can follow us now,' he simply said.

They had to jump over four hyena corpses that were lying on the ground. The Tigress was impressed by how silently the Jaguar and the Leopard had killed them. But she did not have much time to think about it, as the two male predators moved quickly through the tunnel towards the cave entrance.

Suddenly, all hell broke loose. From the other end of the tunnel, coming from the cave entrance, another animal jumped onto the Jaguar, ready to bite his neck. The Jaguar was not prepared for this.

'Stop, Strong Lion,' the Tigress roared at the last moment before the Lion could harm the Jaguar. 'It is me. We have come to rescue the Black Panther, whom your stepfather has caught and imprisoned. As you already know, the Panther and his friends safeguard the Great Waterhole so that the Plague cannot spread. We mean no harm to you, the Young Lioness or the Wise Cat.'

The Lion relaxed his grip on the Jaguar and laughed a dark-sounding laugh that the Tigress had never witnessed before.

'You cannot harm me. No one can harm me. I am Strong Lion, and I will soon become the new ruler of the Tiny Island. The Capricorn vanished without a trace shortly after sunset. I came back from hunting in the night, and the Wise Cat told me that he was gone.

'He must have left in a hurry as the door of the magic chamber was wide open. When I heard that he had disappeared, I immediately tried to follow his tracks. I sensed that he must have used the back entrance as he was not seen going through the front.

'I am now on my way to find him, bring him back and put him on trial. He wanted to spread the Plague in the South of the island, which is where I caught him when he tried to release a cage of rodents. He did not expect me to follow him and track him down. When I confronted him, he denied that the rodents were infected.

'But he could not fool me, and I prevented him from releasing them by throwing the cage into the ocean. He wanted to set them free close to the Energy Point of the South, where animals come every day to strengthen their animal spirit and recharge their energy. He must have become impatient when the Plague did not spread in the way he had planned,' the Lion explained.

'What about the Black Panther? Is he still imprisoned?' the Tigress asked, fearing that something might have happened to him.

'Do not worry,' the Lion answered. 'The Panther is fine. I am only glad that he did not drink the water last night. The Capricorn had poisoned it. He would have died, but he was smart enough not to drink it as he must have sensed that something was wrong with it.

'The Young Lioness is now speaking with him as they have not seen each other for a long time. I am pretty sure that she is trying to find out everything about you, Clumsy Tiger. She is usually very curious,' he added.

The Tigress was unsure for a moment why Strong Lion had called her Clumsy Tiger in front of the other predators. It felt strangely intimate, but she then understood that it was just an old habit of his as he liked to affirm his superiority over her.

'Can we come in please, Strong Lion?' the Tigress asked, trying to refocus her thoughts.

'Yes, of course, please continue along the tunnel to the cave entrance. Tell the Wise Cat that I have let you in and that you have come for the Panther. The Wise Cat will be delighted to meet you finally. And I will catch the Capricorn in the meantime. It is my responsibility to capture him and put him on trial for the evil deeds that he has done for so long on the island.

'The Wise Cat is worried. He took with him all the poisons and magic potions that he had. He could poison the lakes, the soil or even the ocean. The animals of the Tiny Island will not be safe until I catch him. We are facing the Plague now, but we may have to deal with worse things if the Capricorn makes use of his potions before I stop him,' the Lion predicted.

'Should the Desert Leopard and I join you and help you to find the Capricorn?' the Jaguar offered.

'There is no need. I have to do it myself,' the Lion replied.

The Tigress knew that Strong Lion wanted to capture the Capricorn himself. He had suffered the Capricorn's cruelty as a cub, getting gored by his sharp horns countless times, which had left scars both on his skin and on his animal spirit.

The Tigress knew that he had to close this chapter of abuse for himself, and that was why he wanted to catch the Capricorn on his own.

But she was also worried that he was going alone. She would have preferred it if he had accepted the help of the Black Jaguar, but she knew that he was stubborn. It was certain that he would also refuse any help from her.

'I am surprised that you did not meet the Capricorn on your way to the back entrance. He must have hidden in the shadows and passed you without you realising, using magic to neutralise his scent and blur his traces,' the Lion addressed the Jaguar.

'I guess that is the only possibility. No one usually escapes my senses,' the Jaguar responded.

As Strong Lion left to hunt down the Capricorn, the Jaguar, the Cheetah and the Leopard approached the cave entrance.

The Tigress lingered for a moment, watching as Strong Lion vanished. She hoped that he would catch the Capricorn alive and that the Capricorn would not use black magic on him. She was seriously worried.

The Tigress became suddenly aware that some old energy still connected her to the Lion. But the love that she now felt for him was more that of a wise older sister towards her younger brother.

The love she felt for the Black Panther was different. It had a different dimension. Even though they had spent only a little time at the Panther's cave together, she felt secure with him. He was content with who she was, and she sensed that he loved her for being the Tigress, the empress of the Asantian rainforest.

Maybe it was because they had both been through significant trauma and understood that the world was not a place where unicorns met rainbows. Whatever it was, something deeply connected the two of them. Something that she did not understand but felt.

The Tigress' thoughts were interrupted by the voice of the Cheetah.

'Are you coming? Strong Lion has been gone for a while now. We are waiting for you as we do not want to enter the cave without you. It would be impolite, and I do not think the Wise Cat would like it if you were missing. She gets to meet you finally!' the Cheetah roared as she was excited about meeting the Wise Cat as well.

The Tigress woke up. It was as if she had been caught up in a long daydream. She quickly approached the entrance to the cave.

CHAPTER SIXTEEN

Meeting the Wise Cat

The Wise Cat welcomed the four predators. She was waiting at the cave entrance, as if she had known that they were coming.

'Welcome to you, White Tigress, and a warm welcome to your friends. I sensed that you would come to rescue the Black Panther. He told me how you met. Strong Lion freed him after the Capricorn was gone. He talked to the Young Lioness and then to me,' the Wise Cat said.

'But the Panther is already gone. He said that he urgently needed to go back to the Great Waterhole to coordinate with his friends to efficiently prevent the Plague from spreading. He mentioned that it was his duty.

'I am sorry that he has left already. It was interesting talking to him. He has experienced so much in his life that I did not want to break off the conversation. But you also must be disappointed, White Tigress,' she added. It was apparent that the Tigress was not happy at the news.

'That is typical of the Panther,' the Jaguar interrupted their conversation. 'He always thinks that he has to have everything under control. We are all capable of protecting the Great Waterhole, but he thinks that we will be lost without him. I am anyway surprised that he did not break out of the prison. In my experience, nothing stops him from seeking his freedom.'

'There might be an explanation for that. The Capricorn told him that he would be given a fair trial. I also think that the Capricorn must have put a magic potion into his water.

'On the first night, the Panther was extremely restless in his prison. After he had drunk a little water in the morning, he calmed down all of a sudden, and he stayed that way until Strong Lion freed him,' the Wise Cat explained.

'It might have been a bit of both. The Panther likes to follow the rules, and the Capricorn explained to him that he would get a fair trial. That might have calmed him down, but I guess the magic potion also helped,' the Jaguar suggested.

'But now to you, White Tigress,' the Wise Cat addressed her. 'What is your plan? Do you want to stop the Capricorn? I advised Strong Lion to join forces with you to catch the Capricorn, but he refused. The Young Lioness cannot go with him as she is expecting his cubs. You could have helped Strong Lion. But he is stubborn and wants to do it on his own.

'The Capricorn will use his black magic against him. He took with him all the magic potions. I am seriously worried not only about the safety of Strong Lion but also about the safety of the Tiny Island.'

The Wise Cat looked disheartened and tired. The Tigress already knew that the Wise Cat had lost her argument with Strong Lion and that he would not have accepted any help from the Tigress.

The Tigress sensed that he still had a feeling of unease where she was concerned, a feeling of guilt that he had left her, although she had long ago forgiven him and also forgiven herself for not understanding better his wish to have his own lion cubs.

The Young Lioness was calm and understanding with Strong Lion, and that was what the Lion needed in his hot-headedness, not an equally irritable and short-tempered Tigress.

The Tigress was lost in her thoughts but suddenly woke up when the Jaguar said, 'We are leaving immediately. We are going back to the Great Waterhole to find the Panther and to coordinate with him the further protection of the Tiny Island. Otherwise, the Plague will spread, and all our previous efforts will have been in vain.' With those words, the Jaguar and the Leopard exited the cave, leaving the Cheetah and the Tigress behind, baffled by their abrupt departure.

The Wise Cat, however, seemed to have understood. She smiled and explained to them, 'They are now the guardians of the Tiny Island. They have made it their duty to prevent the Black Plague from spreading across the island. They would die for that mission, and they will feel a sense of achievement only when they have stopped the disease from spreading.

'In a way, what they do is questionable, as they kill the animals who come close to the lake. But they do so to prevent the animals across the whole island from getting infected.

'I fear them, but I also admire them. I talked to the

Panther, and I understood that he is performing a task that would be almost impossible for a normal animal.

'He has to do evil to protect the good in this world. He has always done this. Back in Avaria he and his friends protected good, innocent animals from evil creatures who hunted not only for food but for the pure pleasure of killing other animals.

'We each have to follow our own path. The Panther and his friends prevent the evil from spreading in this world; they have an inner calling to protect the innocent. Without them, Avaria would certainly have been a worse place for the animals.

'The animals on the Tiny Island also have to thank them. They not only prevent the Plague from spreading, but also want to bring justice to this world in their determination to fight the evil.

'I am not so sure, however, that it will help their animal spirits, because they fight evil with evil. They sacrifice their inner peace for others to be safe.

'I would not be surprised if the Black Panther joined Strong Lion in his fight against the Capricorn after making sure that everything is under control at the Great Waterhole. I saw the vengeance in his eyes when he left the cave. I knew that he wanted to punish the Capricorn for imprisoning him.

'The Panther seems to have no mercy or forgiveness for those who have wronged him. He believes that he is on the right path, but he is sacrificing his spirit to prevent the evil from spreading everywhere in this world,' the Wise Cat concluded.

'But how can he not see that our animal spirit is the

most precious thing that we have? How can he taint his spirit? Does he not love himself enough? He runs around restlessly to save the whole world. It is a noble cause but one that requires the sacrifice of his own spirit,' the Tigress roared, and one could see tears of despair in her eyes.

'You need to understand that every animal has their path, and they can change it during the course of their life. We all have free will. A few animals find their calling early, and they stick to it their entire life. Other animals, like you, have to go through many transformations to meet their destiny.

'Some animals like to develop their animal spirit. They can teach others how to achieve peace and happiness within themselves. Many animals bring good to this world by taking care of those whom they love.

'Others are the storytellers of this world. They record the good memories that we have shared and the adventures of our lives that we have experienced.

'And some animals are warriors, like the Black Panther, the Black Jaguar and the Desert Leopard. They have committed their lives to fighting the shadow side. They are on the dark side of this world to fight the evil. And often, while saving the world, the dark side consumes them, and they do not find the path back to the light,' the Wise Cat explained.

The Tigress thought about the Wise Cat's words regarding the Panther's sacrifice of his spirit, but she did not say anything.

The Wise Cat continued to express her thoughts, seeming to guess what was in the Tigress' mind.

'White Tigress, I know that you are a warrior of light. You want to save the Panther. You want to show him an alternative path of love, forgiveness and mercy.

'But I can tell you one thing from my experience with the light and the darkness. I was not able to save the animal spirit of the Capricorn, although I tried for a long time wholeheartedly. He chose the path of evil, although there was once light in him as well.

'You will not be able to save the Panther. You were not able to save the Mountain Lion. It was not your fault, for the Mountain Lion did not want to be saved. I tell you now, you cannot save the Panther, even if you try wholeheartedly. You cannot save him because only he can save himself. This is true for every animal when it comes to saving their own animal spirit,' the Wise Cat concluded. She gave the Tigress a look full of compassion.

The Tigress sighed, but she finally understood. It had taken her a long time to understand the path of the Panther, as she had seen it only through her own eyes, not through his.

At that point in time, she finally changed her perspective, and she understood him better now. It was as if a blindfold had been removed while she had listened attentively to the Wise Cat.

'Also, you alone will be able to save yourself. Strong Lion tried to protect you, but he gave up when he understood that only you could save yourself.

'Let me give you this advice: if you save yourself, if you fully forgive yourself for your shortcomings, if you love yourself as you are, then you will also be able to save the Black Panther. Only by saving yourself will you save him.

'But you have to let him go. You have to give him time to heal and to rediscover his animal spirit. Focusing on yourself, for now, will help him to focus on himself. And that will save him. Give him time to heal.

'You can grow and ascend, and he can grow, only if you both focus on yourselves. You have to go your separate ways for now. One day, you may meet again. If it is the right time, you will look into each other's eyes and you will know that it is time to be together.

'You have another transformation to undergo, and you have to prepare for it. I saw it when I looked into the future. You have to grow mentally and spiritually. You have to do it alone. You cannot prepare and at the same time concentrate on rescuing the Panther's spirit.

'If you love yourself, and if you truly love him, let him go for now. Your path leads you away from him so you can succeed in your transformation. And he can grow only if he focuses on his path,' the Wise Cat finished her guidance.

'Thank you, Wise Cat, for your advice. Thank you,' the Tigress said. The tears that ran down her cheeks were soaked up by her white fur. Deep down she knew that the Wise Cat was right and that they had to go their separate ways. The Black Panther had to complete his path and she hers.

'Now I know why everyone calls you the Wise Cat,' the Tigress said. She smiled and bowed her big head in front of the Wise Cat, knowing what she had to do.

The path that she had to follow was not one of happiness and joy but one of loneliness until she reached a state where her animal spirit would allow her to transform again.

'I will take care of Young Leo while you are away, and my spirit will be with you all the time. I am your friend,' the Cheetah said and left the cave after a brief goodbye to the Wise Cat and the Tigress. The Cheetah does not like long goodbyes the same way I do not like them, the Tigress thought and also exited the cave.

— CHAPTER SEVENTEEN —

At the Blue Bay

The Wise Cat's gaze followed the two female predators long after they left, knowing that their paths would be dangerous and difficult. She saw the Cheetah running to her cave in the North, where Young Leo waited for her.

The Tigress took the path to the South, directly to the Blue Bay. She wanted to find the Golden Watersnake as she needed her to break the spiritual bond between Strong Lion and the Tigress. She wanted to let it go once and for all.

Strong Lion was now connected to the Young Lioness, and she to the Panther. The bond with the Lion no longer served her. Although she felt respect for him, she was in love with the Black Panther.

When the Tigress arrived at the Blue Bay, she could not see the Golden Watersnake but sensed her presence. She sat down on the beach and waited for the Watersnake to appear.

Then something strange happened. The Tigress felt that some future danger was looming over the Blue Bay. It was as if the evil had touched her spirit briefly at that moment. She shivered and remembered the Wise Cat saying that the Capricorn had taken with him all his poisons and magic potions and that she was worried that he would do evil with them. He could not carry all of them with him all the time. They were far too numerous. Where would he hide them?

The Tigress' thoughts were interrupted by the appearance of the Golden Watersnake.

'You come to relinquish the bond with Strong Lion?' the Watersnake asked. Clearly she already knew the purpose of her visit. 'Last time, you were still Clumsy Tiger, but now you have ascended to become the White Tigress. I am glad you have. Meeting Strong Lion and saying goodbye to each other was all part of your journey. You grew when you were with each other, but the separation has made both of you stronger. You have finally understood that it was your destiny to be together only for a short while.'

The Tigress was surprised.

'Why did you forge the bond if you already knew that our love would not last for ever? Not having such a powerful connection would have saved me so much pain after Strong Lion left,' the Tigress said and sighed. She did not understand the motives of the Watersnake.

'There was a simple reason for it. I sensed that only you two together could fight the Capricorn. The good had to be united to fight the evil. That is why I forged the bond. You were the strongest apex predators back then, and as a united couple, only you would have been able to fight the Capricorn.

'What I had not considered was that Strong Lion firmly wanted his own lion cubs and that he would not settle for cubs from you.

'Back then, only you were a match for him. There was no lioness on the island. I could not have anticipated that one day the Young Lioness would arrive.

'I cannot break the bond as your animal spirits called for it. You need to understand the following: all animals can connect on a physical, mental or spiritual level.

'Most animals will experience only the physical connection. They mate with each other and have offspring. It is called the circle of life, and without it, the earth would not serve a higher purpose. So, in a way, this level is the most important one; it is the foundation for everything else.

'Some animals, however, have a calling that goes beyond the physical realm. They can forge mental connections. They will collaborate; they may invent great things together; they achieve something that many animals would say was impossible.

'And some animals can connect spiritually. Some of these animals become healers, others become spiritual teachers, and others simply send a message out to the world by being an example to others. Some of them will tell stories of their defeats and victories; they are the chroniclers.

'Very rarely, animals can connect on the third level with all other living creatures. They are called golden animals.

'In the same way, animals can communicate on three levels: physically, mentally and spiritually. Most animals can communicate only physically. They talk to each other using words, gestures and expressions.

'Some animals learn to interact mentally, without using words. They can use telepathy, and they can bridge long distances to talk to each other. There are only a few animals who can connect telepathically. I believe that the Wise Cat, the Capricorn and certainly all golden animals are among them.

'Some can interact at the spiritual level. I think that most animals would be capable of this form of communication, but the absolute majority will experience it only if they have forged a spiritual bond or if they are each other's missing half. But I cannot expand on this now.

'I saw the Capricorn pass by here some time ago. It must have been shortly after sunrise. I do not know what he was looking for. Maybe he was on his way to the Underwater Waterfall. Maybe somewhere else.

'I could not connect to his animal spirit; he was completely closed off. All animals have free will, and they can shield their spirits from others if they wish to. The Capricorn was followed by Strong Lion. I saw him running past the Blue Bay while the sun was still at its peak,' the Golden Watersnake explained.

The Tigress had listened attentively to the Watersnake's words. The Wise Cat had told her similar thoughts in different words before. It all now made sense to her. She had a spiritual bond with Strong Lion because they were both animals who had access to the spiritual realm, and they both felt that they had a higher calling.

With the Black Panther, it was different. When they met each other for the first time, their spirits had connected immediately. The Tigress knew that she had never felt an instant spiritual bond with another animal before. She understood that she had to learn more about it.

'You and Strong Lion have transformed the bond between you already. It is no longer a love connection, but one based on mutual respect. It changed the moment Strong Lion fell in love with the Young Lioness and you fell in love with the Black Panther. You both have found your matching animal spirits.

'That is all I can say on this topic. The bond has already been transformed—and who knows, maybe it will help you one day that you are still connected to Strong Lion. The fight with the Capricorn is imminent, and only if the good animals unite in the fight against the evil do I see hope for the Tiny Island. Otherwise, we will soon see the Capricorn's reign.

'Strong Lion seeks to fight the Capricorn alone. He has prepared for that day. But he may need your help. You know that the Lion is young and reckless and always overestimates his strength.

'And now that the Young Lioness carries his cubs under her heart, she cannot fight. She secures his future, but he will still need a strong ally to fight by his side. And that is likely to be you, whether he wants it or not,' the Golden Watersnake added.

The Tigress now understood that there was no need to relinquish their spiritual connection.

'I will go and search for Strong Lion and help him if you say that this is my destiny,' the Tigress replied.

'You are not prepared for this fight yet. Your spirit

needs to transform to be ready as the evil is powerful in the Capricorn. You will not be able to defeat him with your strength and wit alone. You need to develop your animal spirit.

'You need to find the Golden Hare, who lives at the Energy Point of the South. He will teach you how to meditate and strengthen your spirit and the light inside you. He will teach you how to be patient and how you can let go of your anger and tame your wild nature.

'Please go to the Golden Hare! He already awaits you. And he will show you how to gather the strength within you to become the animal you are truly capable of being,' the Watersnake finished her explanation.

The Tigress was not surprised. The Wise Cat had already mentioned another transformation. The Tigress thanked the Golden Watersnake, who vanished without a further goodbye.

The Tigress understood that the Watersnake wanted her to go to the Energy Point. She had never met the Golden Hare before, but she sensed that only he could prepare her for the next transformation.

She no longer questioned any advice given to her by the golden animals. She knew that they were essential guides as they helped animals to transform and ascend in their spirit. She had forgotten where precisely the Energy Point was since her last visit a very long time ago with the Mountain Lion, but once in the South, she knew she would feel its presence.

Suddenly, she felt the Panther's spirit. She stood still and focused her mind on him.

Are you alright? I am worried about you. Are you managing to contain the Black Plague? she asked mentally.

Yes, I am keeping my head above water. I am tired, but everything is under control, she heard his voice in her mind.

She felt that the Panther had fully immersed himself in his task of keeping the Plague under control and that it would cost him his whole energy. When she brought her focus back to herself, she realised that they had communicated telepathically for the first time.

CHAPTER EIGHTEEN

The Energy Point of the South

When the Tigress arrived at the Energy Point of the South, the Golden Hare greeted her.

'I see you travelled fast. The Golden Watersnake foretold your arrival. I will teach you how to align your body, mind and spirit so you can undergo your final transformation.

'You will not be able to choose your animal spirit this time; it will choose you. You will have to stay here for seven nights to prepare. Please lie down and sleep. It is time to rest. You will require all your strength for the exercises. We will start the practice in the morning,' the Hare introduced himself.

The Tigress immediately trusted him and did as she was told. She was tired from the long journey and happy that she could rest.

It was a moonless night, with the stars shining brightly. Not long after she fell asleep, she found herself in a dream.

She saw the Black Panther, who was patrolling around the Great Waterhole. He looked tired and sad. She could feel that the task of preventing the Plague from spreading had deeply wounded his spirit as he had to kill the infected animals.

She also saw Young Leo and instantly knew that he missed his mother.

Later, the Mountain Lion appeared and said to her: *Continue to follow your path, and you will succeed. I am sorry that I could no longer be there for you and Leo, but I had to follow my path. I hope you will forgive me one day.*

Then she fell into a deep, dreamless sleep.

When the Tigress awoke the next morning, the Golden Hare told her that they should start the practice to strengthen her body, mind and spirit.

When he showed her the various exercises, the Tigress was surprised that the small Hare had such strength. He claimed that it all had to do with his strong animal spirit.

Then they practised meditation together. The Tigress' mind kept going back to the Panther. She understood that he had not only helped her to heal her body; being with him had also healed her animal spirit.

She sensed, however, that it was difficult for the Black Panther to accept the healing that she could give him. So they had to part to follow their own paths.

For the Panther, this was to prevent the Black Plague from spreading; for the Tigress, it was to transform in her spirit once again to be able to fight an even more dangerous disease: the pure evil that was embodied in the Capricorn. She knew that she would have to face the Capricorn if Strong Lion was unable to defeat him.

The meditation sessions were demanding, but the Tigress could not focus. It was difficult for her to think nothing, and her thoughts wandered whenever she closed her eyes.

First, she thought of the Panther. She was still fascinated by their telepathic communication and wondered what he was doing. But she could not connect to him this time.

Perhaps she could reach out on a mental level only when he was focused on her at the same time. She decided to ask the Hare about this, once they had finished their meditation.

Then her thoughts wandered to Young Leo. Although she knew that he was happy being at the Cheetah's cave, she still felt guilty. There was too much going on in her life. She had to take care of so many things. She had to hunt for her little family, but she also had to make sure that the Tiny Island was a safe place.

And currently, it was not. She asked herself why she could not just have a quiet life like many other animals. Instead, she had embarked on another adventure and left Leo with someone else, as she had done so often recently.

She thought that maybe she was a terrible mother. First, she had wanted to reclaim the Great Waterhole for the other animals, almost dying in the process.

Then, she had gone out to rescue the Black Panther from his imprisonment. Now, she was on a mission to prepare for her last transformation.

Probably she would also have to save the reckless Lion, who thought he could fight the Capricorn alone.

Sometimes, life was just difficult, but she knew that she would never give up. That was the character trait for which she admired the Panther most. He never gave up; he fought for his cause even if the situation appeared hopeless.

And he always found a solution, even if he had to overcome immense obstacles. He was a real apex predator who mastered every challenge in his life, and who still had patience and endurance, even if the reward was far away.

They were very much alike in their endurance and also in their ability to suffer. The Tigress missed him badly, and all she wished for at that moment was to be in a quiet cave together with Leo and the Panther, just being a complete family. This was the first time since the Mountain Lion had died that she'd had this feeling.

The Golden Hare hit a gong as a sign that the Tigress should come back to reality.

'Fine?' he asked, as he always did when finishing a meditation or strengthening exercise.

'I could not concentrate much,' the Tigress replied and sighed.

'That is normal. Although the ultimate aim is to empty our mind while meditating, it does not happen until we are experienced in the art of meditation.

'The trick is accepting that those thoughts are coming and going and detaching from them after we think them. I will do the following exercise with you.

'First, I will lend you my ear, and then we will speak about your thoughts while you were meditating. Then, we will try again, and this time you will concentrate on just one word that you choose, and you will slowly repeat it in your mind.

'And after that, we will do a strengthening exercise and then meditate again,' the Hare guided the Tigress, who had so many questions for him and realised that she had already been contemplating them for a long time.

The Tigress felt that the Hare was the right animal with whom she could discuss them.

'I often feel that I am a bad mother. I used to spend so much time with Leo when his father, the Mountain Lion, was still alive. Now I need to hunt on my own and take care of the needs of Leo.

'Often, he makes it difficult for me, as I have to hunt for him as if he were still a little cub. At times, however, he already behaves pridefully, like a grown-up male lion. He must have copied this behaviour from Strong Lion when he still came regularly to our cave.

'And if that were not enough, there is always some emergency. When the Lion and I were the strongest animals on the island, it always fell to us to get involved in trouble and fight off the threat.

'After the predators from Avaria came, I hoped that things would calm down a bit as they had taken on the task of protecting the Tiny Island. The moment they arrived and luckily prevented the Plague from spreading, they did the animals a great favour.

'However, at the same time, the evil became stronger. There are rumours that the Capricorn has been able to gather many more animals behind him,' the Tigress explained.

The Golden Hare thought about the things the Tigress had told him and answered calmly after what seemed like a lifetime.

'I believe that you are a good mother, after all. You have always given your best and used your time wisely by spending it with Cub Leo when the Mountain Lion was providing for you. You also made the right decision after he died in moving far away from the White Mountains to start a new life.

'I also do not think that it was a poor decision to fall in love with Strong Lion. Falling in love is never a poor decision, and it was good for Leo to see the example of the Lion, even if he is prideful and often reckless. He is still an apex predator, and he showed Leo a few tricks. Of course, it hurt not only you but also your cub when Strong Lion left, but it also showed Leo that life is a constant process of coming and going.

'You should also be happy that you now have the Black Panther in your life. Although he is busy protecting the Tiny Island, he will make a good example for Leo. The Panther is more mature than Strong Lion, and he knows how to use his strength. He will be able to teach Leo a lot.

'You, the Black Panther and Young Leo have one thing in common. You have already experienced your fair share of pain. You will be more patient and forgiving towards each other and accept each other's flaws much better as a result. Remember that the Lion was young and impatient and that he could not accept your shortcomings,' the Hare concluded.

The Tigress realised only then that the Golden Hare already seemed to know her life story. But she decided to stop wondering about this. The golden animals had an understanding of the world that was beyond the comprehension of even the wisest animals.

'I feel strongly bound to the spirit of the Panther, and we started to communicate telepathically when I was on my way to you. What is the magic behind this telepathy? You seem to know, and you also seem to be able to read my mind!' she said and smiled, even though she felt uneasy.

'It is simple and complicated at the same time. The golden animals are connected to all other animals in this world, and we can reach out to their spirits. I cannot read your mind. But your animal spirit told me your story while we were meditating.

'A very few other animals can also communicate telepathically, and their minds connect. The golden animals have mastered the craft, but animals such as the Wise Cat and the Wise Owl are capable of it, too. Unfortunately, evil spirits such as the Capricorn have also mastered it,' the Golden Hare finished his explanation.

'But why could I communicate telepathically with the Panther?' the Tigress asked, determined to know everything.

'With him and you, things are a little more complicated. You might be each other's missing half— but I cannot really say whether that is the case or not.

'As the legend goes, a very long time ago, when the first animals appeared on earth, some animals were not at peace with themselves. They experienced an inner struggle—the good and the bad were fighting within them—and they could not decide which side to be on. There will always be a good and an evil side, as there has to be balance. When the good is strengthened, the evil usually also becomes stronger.

'So, the Universal Divine Spirit decided to help those animals who were torn inside. He had to make sure that balance was maintained. At first, he thought to take out all the evil parts and attribute them to one animal spirit and all the good ones and attribute them to another.

'But then the Universal Divine Spirit understood in his eternal wisdom that this was not fair because the good spirit would have no chance to develop and ascend. After all, they would already be so pure. Likewise, the evil animal spirit would have no opportunity to become good, as there would simply be no good in them. So he decided that all spirits should have the seeds of good and evil in them.

'Those spirits that had a strong good and a powerful evil side were divided into two animal spirits. In this way, the Universal Divine Spirit balanced out the two sides. It helped to tame their wild nature.

'The division of the spirits had two interesting effects, which we can still experience today. Each of the now-divided spirits could choose to follow the path of darkness or the path of light. They had both sides in themselves.

'Some of them chose the eternal path of evil; others chose the path of good.

'But most of them were thrown from one path to the other during their lifetime. Sometimes they started on the path of light but were then distracted and fell prey to greed, anger, envy or pride.

'Some could, however, return to the path of light when they were humbled by adverse events affecting them, thereby developing gratitude, forgiveness and love. Others received help to return to the path of light, often in the form of other animals who guided them.

'Some stayed on the shadow side until their life ended. Often, they were so busy fuelling their anger, envy, greed or pride that they rejected the help of other animals. Sometimes, it was almost tragic.

'If you think of the Capricorn, he had the Wise Cat on his side to return to the light. But he chose not to because his spirit was poisoned by the feeling of power that he had over other animals with his black magic.

'The other effect that the division of the animal spirits had was more sublime. However, it had a profound impact on those animals in their search for their path. Those animal spirits had a force inside them that was at the same time a blessing and a curse.

'The divided spirits that were separated aeons ago were inevitably drawn to each other. For as long as they did not meet, they were subconsciously searching for their missing other half, thereby entering into many adventures, suffering many misfortunes and facing many adversities until, by chance or by destiny, they met one day. From that day onwards, they were magnetically attracted to one another.

'When they met, they often had, for the first time in their animal life, the feeling of wholeness. Something inside their animal spirit changed at that moment.

'If the two parts of the same spirit were of the opposite sex and the same animal species, things were easy. They found each other, fell in love, mated and usually had a life together. Although they also faced external challenges, those two animals could normally not be separated because their love was strong.

'If those spirits were siblings, they usually had a powerful connection and often were inseparable for their whole lifespan, even though they went on to create their own families. Sometimes twin spirits only became friends, but those friendships would be deep and remain their whole animal life.

'Things were a little trickier when the animals found their twin spirit in a different animal species. Although such unions are not rare, they are not common either. The two animals must be open to them. They happen more often among apex predators.

'You, Tigress, for example, first followed the Mountain Lion to the White Mountains, and then you were together with Strong Lion. And after he left, you met the Black Panther. All three belong to a different animal species than you and they have very different animal spirits,' the Hare pointed out.

The Tigress had listened well to what the Golden Hare had to say. She understood better now why she had

had to take her life path and why she had had to face those challenges and adventures.

She finally realised why those three very different predators had crossed her path. The Mountain Lion had been an ideal partner for creating a family. Strong Lion had shown her that it was important to fulfil our destiny and that we need to follow what we believe in, whether it is starting a family or something else.

With the Black Panther, it was more complicated. He was mysterious, and she did not entirely understand his path. He came from a place of light, had dived deep into the world of the shadows and was now trying to find his way back to the light.

At the same time, he took on tasks that most animals would not, and while doing so, he continued to let darkness into his life. His path seemed a difficult one, almost like a self-inflicted burden.

Although he had nothing to prove to himself, he had the urge to bring balance to the world. He wanted to fight for the good animals, but in doing so, he had crossed the line and gone to the dark side.

Maybe it was he who could teach her how to release her shadows. She needed to understand better why their paths had crossed, but she already had a theory.

'Do you really think that the Black Panther is the missing other half of my animal spirit?' the Tigress asked the Golden Hare.

'I think that you can only know this for yourself. Follow your instincts; follow your intuition. You already know that you are a gift to each other. Deep inside your spirit, you already know whether he is your missing half. One day, it will be fully revealed to both of you,' he answered and closed his eyes to prepare for another meditation.

The Tigress understood that they had to embark on another meditation and closed her eyes as well.

'With your eyes closed, we will now chant the universal mantra "Om" together three times with full devotion, and then we will start to meditate. You may continue to repeat the mantra silently,' the Hare directed the Tigress.

'Om, om, om,' they chanted in unison, and the high voice of the Tigress and the deeper voice of the Hare sounded loud across the savannah of the South.

'Please lie down in a comfortable position and breathe in and out slowly,' the Hare instructed the Tigress.

During the meditation, the Tigress focused only on repeating the mantra and sank into a deep meditative trance. It was as if the universe had opened for her. She stayed in the present moment and felt one with the nature surrounding her.

It was as if her animal spirit had exited her body, and she saw herself from above lying in deep meditation. She saw her body for what it was: a vessel that was there so that she could fulfil the purpose for which she had been born.

She then saw the Black Panther, who was intensely involved in his daily routine. Seeing him in her meditative state gave her a profound sense of peace.

Only moments later the Hare hit the gong, and the Tigress emerged slowly from her trance.

'Fine?' he asked. The Tigress only nodded silently. She was still moved by what she had experienced during the meditation.

'Tomorrow, before sunrise, we will continue our practice. I am sure if you continue to practise the meditation, you will master the art of telepathy as well and be ready for your next transformation.

'Now, sleep. This day was exhausting for both of us. I do not have many guests that stay overnight. Many animals have forgotten that the Energy Point can give them immense strength,' the Hare concluded before he closed his eyes and slept instantly.

Over the following days, the Tigress and the Hare practised strengthening and breathing exercises and meditation. She felt every muscle in her body.

Although those exercises were easy for her in the beginning, doing them for most of the day required all her strength. The meditations in between the physical practices, however, released the tension that had built up.

'Tomorrow, I will show you a special meditation. I will teach you how to release your shadows and embrace the light.

'Do you see the two circles and the two signposts? They exactly describe how to release your shadows and embrace the light. You can do it in a meditation exercise, but for most animals, it is easier if they go around the circles and chant the mantras.

I release :

1- my fears

2- my guilts

3- my angers

4- my sorrows

5- my lies

6- my illusions

7- my attachments

I call forth within me

1- trust

2- creativity

3- will

4- love

5- truth

6- light

7- letting go

'They usually walk around the first circle seven times. What they have to say or repeat mentally is written on the first signpost. They have to release their fears, feelings of guilt and anger, sorrows, lies, illusions and attachments. That means they let go of the shadows that are holding them back.

'By walking in the second circle seven times while reciting the mantras, they embrace and strengthen the light inside them. They call forth within them trust, creativity, will, love, truth, light and letting go.

'Sleep now! Tomorrow will be an important day for you,' the Hare said before the Tigress rested.

The Tigress slept early that evening as she was exhausted. She was excited to learn about the special meditation. She had learned a lot from the Golden Hare, not only regarding the meditation and the breathing and strengthening exercises, but also about how body, mind and spirit had to be whole and aligned to walk the path of light.

The Hare gave her only a mix of vegetables and seeds to eat, but interestingly, they gave her even more strength. She respected this unusual form of diet for her as she did not want to offend the Hare by catching fish while she was at the Energy Point.

It was a sacred place, and it was inappropriate for her to eat any other animal, even though it was her nature to hunt. She thought that this must be part of the cleansing process that the Golden Hare wanted her to go through.

During the night, something strange happened. The Tigress again had one of those nights when she slept poorly. She slipped in and out of sleep and moved her paws restlessly. When she finally fell into a deep sleep, she had a vivid dream about Strong Lion.

Close to the extinct volcano, she saw him fighting with a Red Firedragon, who breathed fire at the Lion time after time, burning his fur and skin. The Lion was lying helpless on the rocks close to the foot of the volcano and looked to be either dead or seriously wounded, as he was not moving.

A shock wave went through the Tigress' body, and she was immediately wide awake. She felt the intense pain of burned skin and instantly knew that it was the pain that the Lion was experiencing at that moment. He must be calling me for help, she thought. The Golden Watersnake had been right: the bond between her and the Lion now served an important purpose.

The Hare was awake and meditating. The Tigress interrupted his meditation impatiently and quickly told him about her dream.

'I think it is real! I think it is happening right now. Strong Lion has called me to help him. I must leave immediately. Hopefully, I will find him while he is still alive,' the Tigress said, almost shouting at the Hare.

'You are not ready yet. You have not advanced far enough with your exercises. If you go now to find Strong Lion, you may not be able to survive a transformation as it requires immense strength to undertake the final transformation. You may not be able to save the Lion, and you are too weak to face the Red Firedragon as the White Tigress. He will burn you in the same way he has burned the Lion,' the Golden Hare answered calmly. For the first time, he looked not happy but worried.

'But I have to try. I cannot just sit here and meditate while Strong Lion is dying. He is expecting his cubs soon. He needs to be there as a father and as the alpha of his pride,' the Tigress replied.

She thought of the Mountain Lion and how he could no longer be there for Young Leo because of his greed. Strong Lion might die because of his pride in wanting to face the Capricorn alone.

'I understand that you want to rescue your friend, but you should keep in mind that sometimes it is more important to honour a higher cause, as your transformation may help you to fight the Red Firedragon.

'And you might be the only one who can fight him. But you have to follow your path; you have to follow your intuition,' the Golden Hare concluded. The Tigress felt that he had nothing to add.

'Thank you for preparing me for the transformation. I am sad that I could not finish my practice, especially the meditation regarding the release of the shadows. My intuition, however, tells me that I should leave now and find Strong Lion,' the Tigress answered.

'So farewell! May the Universal Divine Spirit be with you on your chosen path,' the Hare said and vanished.

The White Tigress was alone at the Energy Point of the South. She did not question why the Hare had disappeared in front of her eyes.

The golden animals were an inexplicable mystery to her that could not be solved. She refocused her thoughts and instantly set out for the foot of the extinct volcano. She knew that it would take her some time to reach there and that she would have to be fast to find the Lion alive.

CHAPTER NINETEEN

The Red Firedragon

While the White Tigress was staying at the Energy Point to prepare for her final transformation, Strong Lion followed the path of the Capricorn.

It was difficult for him to find the Capricorn, who was using magic to blur his tracks, for the Capricorn understood that the Lion would follow him to get his revenge. But Strong Lion used his intuition, as he knew his stepfather well.

The Lion felt prepared as he was stronger than the Capricorn. All his magic had not helped his stepfather against him in the past; only one time had the Capricorn succeeded—when he had separated the Lion and the Tigress. Strong Lion understood that this had been destiny. Anyway, he was content that the Tigress and he had parted ways because he had finally found his Lioness, who now carried his cubs.

The Tigress represented competition as she was as strong as he was and displayed the same kind of stubbornness and impatience, whereas the Young Lioness calmed him down.

Deep in his thoughts, he stumbled across the footprints of the Capricorn at the bottom of the volcano. *The Capricorn is getting old, and his magic touch is fading,* the Lion thought and smiled at his luck.

But had the Capricorn left footprints intentionally? Strong Lion did not give this possibility much thought. Ahead of him lay a steep track to the Crater Lake, which would be difficult for a heavy lion to climb. He was, however, determined and did not shy away from this challenge.

In the meantime, the Capricorn had made his way up to the lake, which was on top of the volcano. He sensed that someone was following him. It was probably Strong Lion.

'Soon, I will be the sole ruler of the Tiny Island, and no one will be able to challenge me, not Strong Lion, not the White Tigress nor the Black Panther, no one!' the Capricorn shouted when he reached the lake.

If any animal had heard him, they would have thought that he had gone insane. But he felt invincible. His plan was indeed flawless, as the Lion would soon find out.

Immediately after the Capricorn reached the lake, he started his preparations. He put on the ground a circle of black candles, lit them and then sat inside the circle. He entered into a deep meditative state, humming strange words.

Meanwhile, the Lion had almost climbed up the path leading to the top. He saw the Capricorn from afar, sitting on the shore of the Crater Lake. Soon he would reach him.

Anger and even hatred for the Capricorn was rising in Strong Lion's heart.

Anger and hatred for the harsh time as a cub, when the Capricorn had abused his powers as a stepfather.

Anger and hatred for the time that had been wasted because the Capricorn had prevented him from becoming the new ruler of the Tiny Island.

All the resentment that the Lion had built up inside suddenly erupted as he started running towards the Capricorn, roaring furiously.

But the Capricorn was utterly unfazed. He slowly stood up when he saw the raging Lion approaching to show that he did not fear him.

Shortly before Strong Lion could reach him, he jumped into the lake, leaving behind the baffled Lion. The Crater Lake was deep. The Capricorn, with his massive horns, sank fast, and the Lion could no longer see him.

Strong Lion did not understand. Had the Capricorn so feared his rage that he had decided to die in the cold floods of the Crater Lake? Why had the Capricorn not put up a fight?

Although the Lion was convinced his strength would allow him to defeat the Capricorn, he still dreaded his magic. Why had he been sitting in this circle of black candles, which blew out the moment that the Capricorn jumped into the lake?

Strong Lion waited for a while, but when the Capricorn did not make his way out of the lake, he assumed that he had drowned.

The sunset was fast approaching. The Lion started running to reach the foot of the volcano before it was completely dark. But he should have been more careful and should not have underestimated the Capricorn.

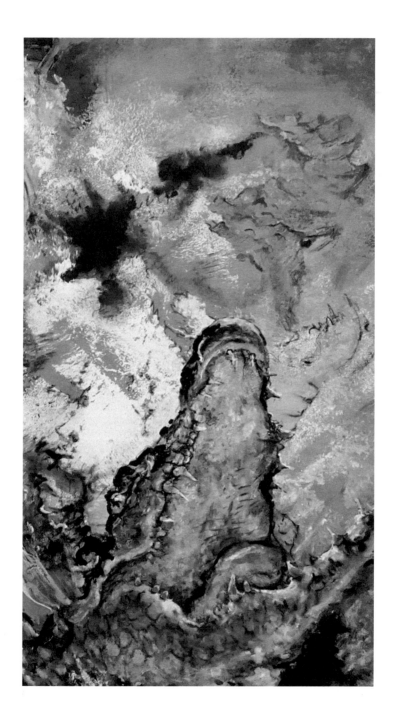

As soon as he turned his back to the Crater Lake, the water in the lake started to move, and a giant vortex appeared.

At first, the vortex seemed to suck in the water of the Crater Lake, but the next moment it reversed and spat out a Red Firedragon, who shot up into the sky and spun around, flapping his giant wings. Then he hissed and breathed his first blast of fire.

The Lion turned around when he heard the beat of the huge wings. Strong Lion's brave heart froze as he looked directly into the cold eyes of the Firedragon.

He instantly knew that it would be a fight to the death, and his mind started spinning. I have clearly underestimated the Capricorn, and now I may have to pay the price, he thought.

Fear crept into the Lion's heart as he acknowledged that if he lost the fight, he would never see his unborn cubs. But he would not have been Strong Lion if that fear had remained for long. He simply could not have anticipated this kind of transformation.

Now the ugly creature who had once been his stepfather started breathing fire at him. Strong Lion had to run a serpentine path down the volcano to avoid being hit by the flames.

At first, the fire that the Firedragon breathed from his mouth was not precise, but his aim became more accurate each time. However, as he had to generate fire in his lungs, the Lion had enough time to run in between the blasts.

Strong Lion was intelligent and counted the time between one fire blast and the next to anticipate when he could run and when he had to hide behind a big rock.

The moment that the Firedragon flew too low, the Lion jumped up and bit his tail. The Red Firedragon screamed, but then he managed to shake off the Lion.

Strong Lion knew instinctively that he had to attack the Firedragon's neck. Only then would he stand a small chance against him.

The next time the Firedragon came close to him, Strong Lion sprang into the air, putting all his strength into the jump and burrowing his teeth deeply into his enemy's neck.

The Firedragon fell to the ground, and the two predators rolled down the volcano, intertwined with each other. Finally, the Firedragon freed himself from the Lion's jaws. Full of fury, he breathed fire towards the Lion that burned his fur and skin.

Strong Lion remained on the ground. He had been defeated even though he had fought bravely. Soon he would die, and the Firedragon claimed the victory. He did not want to finish off the Lion with another blast as he enjoyed the thought that he would die slowly, painfully and alone. He could hear the Lion groaning in pain and hissed spitefully.

The Red Firedragon left the volcano and flew back towards the Secret Caves, where he would meet his followers. The caves were in the Northeast of the island and formed of lava stones. Depending on the tide, it could be difficult to reach them.

On his way, he thought that he might kill the Tigress first as her cave was close to the Secret Caves. Maybe he could surprise her. He would not hesitate to kill Young Leo as he could not risk leaving the offspring of the Tigress alive.

When he reached the Tigress' cave, no one was there. What he did not know was that she had left Young Leo with the Cheetah in the North.

The Firedragon was disappointed. He could no longer sense the presence of the White Tigress, the Wise Cat or the Young Lioness.

I must have lost my psychic ability to know the physical location of animals when I transformed into the Red Firedragon, he thought and was confused. He was, however, not overly worried as he was now much stronger than before and could breathe fire. He then recalled from the White Mountains that every transformation at the Black Rock required an animal to leave something behind. The same must apply for the Crater Lake.

He was confident that he would no longer need that particular psychic ability, and he still knew his magic formulas and how to make magic potions. Anyhow, he would soon have defeated all his enemies with his newly gained strength.

By the time the Red Firedragon reached the Secret Caves, his followers had already arrived. Before leaving for the volcano, he had commanded the Black Falcon to spread the word that they should be ready.

Among the animals on the evil side, there were three elephants, poisonous snakes, buffalos, hyenas, black and white rhinos, hippos, crocodiles and wolves.

Before going to the Great Waterhole to fight the Black Panther and his friends, he had to undertake one more task.

On the way to the lake, they would stop at his former cave and find the Young Lioness as he would spare neither her nor her unborn cubs.

The Firedragon took pleasure from the thought that he would kill them and that his dying stepson could do nothing about it. And if he was lucky, he would also get hold of the Wise Cat.

He and the Wise Cat had hated each other for a long time. He could never kill her before as her white magic was as strong as his black magic. There was a balance between them. Now, however, he was sure he would finally be able to defeat her.

CHAPTER TWENTY

Transformations

Strong Lion's heart was full of regret and fear. Regret that he would not see the Young Lioness again and his soon-to-be-born cubs. Regret that he had been too prideful and had not allowed the Tigress to join him in his fight. Together, they would have stood a chance against the Firedragon.

Fear that the Firedragon would kill the Lioness and his unborn cubs and would soon become the merciless new ruler of the Tiny Island.

Then his thoughts wandered to the Tigress. The last two times he had seen her, she had no longer been Clumsy Tiger but a true empress of the savannah.

Although the island was unfamiliar territory to her, she had mastered the task not only of surviving but of actually thriving. She had levelled up, and that was shown by her transformation into the White Tigress.

Strong Lion now remembered the bond that the Golden Watersnake had forged between them. He still felt this connection sometimes. Suddenly, he could feel the Tigress' animal spirit. He wanted to say goodbye as he sensed that his strength would fade soon.

Of course, that was the moment when the Tigress had the dream about the Lion, when she woke up and followed her intuition to find him.

The Tigress ran as fast as she could. Not long after she had left the Energy Point of the South, she reached the volcano. She heard a faint groaning and instantly knew that it was Strong Lion. When she approached the dying Lion in the dark, she did not immediately see how badly wounded he was.

'Strong Lion, it is me. I saw you fighting with a Red Firedragon in my dream, and I felt you needed my help,' she said.

'I no longer need your help,' the Lion replied. 'I am dying, and there is nothing you can do about it. The Capricorn transformed into the Red Firedragon and burned my whole body with his fire. Please go quickly and rescue the Young Lioness and our unborn cubs. Only you can do it; only you can defeat him.'

The Tigress came closer. Now she saw his bleeding wounds. He was right, she thought, he would soon be dead.

Still, the Tigress did not consider giving up. She could not leave him behind. Her intuition told her that there was a reason he had called her and that it had nothing to do with saving the Lioness.

The Tigress knew that the Wise Cat could foresee the future. She would most likely have taken precautions to move the pregnant Lioness to a safe place. She was also sure that the Wise Cat would reach out telepathically if help was needed.

The Tigress put her paw on the Lion's paw compassionately.

'Please tell me quickly how the Capricorn managed to transform into the Red Firedragon. The Underwater

Waterfall is too far away for him to have undertaken it there,' she prompted him.

Although Strong Lion wanted the Tigress to save the Lioness, it occurred to him that he had to tell the Tigress the story of the Capricorn's transformation.

Maybe she would find a way to defeat the Firedragon. He also felt deep in his spirit that the Tigress' strength had increased even further than when he had last seen her. He could feel her raw energy, and her sheer presence was almost intimidating.

Quickly, Strong Lion told her how he had seen the Capricorn meditate in a circle of black candles and then jump into the Crater Lake before he came out as the Red Firedragon.

That was all the information that the Tigress needed.

'The Crater Lake must be another way to transform your animal spirit. It must be even more powerful than the Underwater Waterfall. I have never before heard of an animal transforming into a dragon,' she said swiftly.

She instinctively knew that her final transformation, too, had to take place in the Crater Lake and not in the Underwater Waterfall.

'I am also destined to transform in the lake as I cannot fight such a strong creature as the Red Firedragon as the White Tigress,' she told the Lion.

'Please go quickly and save the Young Lioness!' the Lion pleaded sincerely.

'I will go, but I will not go alone. I will drag you with me, as the Crater Lake is your only chance of survival. You, too, need to transform in the lake to be there for the Young Lioness and soon also your cubs. I will not leave you behind,' the Tigress replied. She was on fire now. She would leave no one behind.

'Please do not bother with me. Go alone. You cannot lose any more valuable time,' Strong Lion begged.

The White Tigress did not argue further with the Lion. She knew that it was pointless because he was so stubborn, and he would die stubbornly.

Instead, with one move, she swung the Lion onto her back and started to carry him towards the Crater Lake. As Strong Lion fell into unconsciousness at that moment, he did not offer any resistance.

She was strong now, much stronger than she expected. Although the Lion was heavy, the Tigress carried him up the steep path leading to the top.

The sun had already risen when she reached the Crater Lake. Carefully, she laid down the Lion, who was still breathing but unconscious.

The Tigress tried to wake him, but he did not respond. She had to act swiftly; otherwise, the Lion would die in her paws. Knowing that it was his only chance, she took Strong Lion and dived with him into the Crater Lake.

At incredible speed, the strong force of a water vortex pulled them both down. The Tigress almost lost consciousness, and the Lion's body slipped through her paws. She saw two Giant Eels wrap themselves around his body, dragging him deep down, and then propelling him rapidly upwards.

The same happened to her. Two Giant Eels came, wrapped themselves around her body, dragged her down, and then propelled her up to the waterline. She reached the shore of the lake and fell into unconsciousness.

CHAPTER TWENTY-ONE

The White Dragon

When she woke up, she slowly opened her eyes and looked at the bright sunlight. She was alive but must have been unconscious for some time.

'Thank you. You rescued me,' she heard a familiar voice behind her. When she turned her head, she saw a huge White Lion.

That must be Strong Lion, she thought, and was happy that he had survived and ascended. That meant he had more strength now. Together they would be able to fight the Red Firedragon.

'So how is it to have wings?' the Lion asked.

She was surprised. What did he mean? She looked down at herself for the first time and could see that she, too, had transformed. She was no Tigress now but a beautiful White Dragon.

'What should I call you?' the Lion asked. He seemed excited that the Tigress had transformed into a dragon.

'I think I am going to continue calling you Clumsy Tiger even if you are no longer clumsy. At least you have not lost your beautiful green eyes,' the Lion joked.

'I am the White Dragon,' she replied. She felt confident and secure. She was not even fazed by the Lion's flirtatious comment. She knew that it was his nature and that he could do nothing about it.

'Please try to breathe fire. Maybe you are also capable of breathing fire, like the Red Firedragon. Together we can defeat him,' the Lion roared, and his voice boomed full of confidence.

The White Dragon breathed in and out a couple of times, as she had learned from her meditation practice. After three breaths, she pushed a blast of white light out of her mouth. It burned the grass in front of her.

'That is amazing. You have a white flame that can burn things. Exciting!' the Lion said. Now the Dragon knew that the Lion was still the young and reckless predator who got excited so quickly. She smiled at him and showed her white teeth.

'We need to go to your cave right now. We have to find the Wise Cat and the Young Lioness. We may have to save them. Come! We cannot waste time,' she replied.

The White Dragon did not have to tell him twice as the Lion knew that his mate's and his stepmother's lives were at stake. The Red Firedragon would not spare them—he would take pleasure in killing them. The Lion was deeply worried that his stepfather had such power now. They had to act fast; otherwise, everything would be lost.

The White Dragon started flying towards the Lion's cave while the Lion ran directly below her. Although she flew quickly, the Lion could keep pace.

Soon they reached the cave and searched for the Young Lioness and the Wise Cat, but they could not find either of them.

The Dragon used her newly discovered telepathic abilities to reach out to the Black Panther. Finally, she sensed him and was happy to connect to his mind. Without needing any communication, she then touched his spirit as it gave her a sense of peace. She could feel that the Panther was in a state of high alertness.

Then her animal spirit wandered effortlessly to the Wise Cat, who seemed alert but somehow also peaceful. The White Dragon understood that she and the Young Lioness were safe in the Panther's cave. She also sensed incredible joy in the Wise Cat's spirit. The Young Lioness must have given birth to the cubs, she acknowledged.

The Dragon's heart filled with joy. She was happy that new life had been born amidst adversity. It gave her hope to know that even in the worst of times, the wheel of life continued to spin.

'The Young Lioness and the Wise Cat are both safe in the Panther's cave. And congratulations, the Young Lioness has just given birth to your cubs,' she told the Lion and smiled. She was happy that she could give him such good news.

The Lion roared with joy that he was a father now. The White Dragon knew at that moment that it was not only females who could have an incredible sense of happiness when they gave birth. Male animals, too, could feel great joy if their sincerest wish was to have their own cubs.

'We must leave immediately and find the Young Lioness, the cubs and the Wise Cat. I need to protect them,' he said. The Lion's voice boomed with confidence now that he was a father and had to protect his cubs and their mother.

'Yes,' the White Dragon said briefly before they headed towards the Great Waterhole. She struggled to keep up with the Lion, who stormed off at an extraordinary speed to meet his cubs for the first time. It was either good fortune or destiny that they did not encounter the enemy's army.

Shortly after they had left, the Red Firedragon reached his former cave. Neither the Young Lioness nor the Wise Cat was there, he noticed with disappointment. He decided, however, that he could kill them later as there was no chance that they could escape him now that Strong Lion was dead.

The Firedragon used the stop to swear in his army.

'I need you to fight. I need you to fight to the death, if necessary. Anyone I see running in the other direction will die slowly. We will not retreat until the last of our enemies is dead.

'And you need to bring me the White Tigress as I want to kill her personally. Strong Lion is already dead. Soon we will defeat the enemy!' the Red Firedragon roared.

'Hurray!' the battle cry sounded dangerously across the savannah. All those animals who heard it from afar went scared into hiding.

CHAPTER TWENTY-TWO

The Circle of Life

As the White Dragon and the Lion approached the Panther's cave, they could already hear the sound of lion cubs. It was a whispered meow, softer than the sound of little kittens.

The Lion stormed inside without taking notice of the two guards who were stationed at the entrance. When he entered, his heart almost stopped. Three cubs jumped up and down between the paws of the Young Lioness. She licked them and smiled the smile of a happy new mother.

'I am relieved to see you. I was concerned that you would struggle to fight the Capricorn with his black magic. Look how beautiful our cubs are,' the Lioness said and smiled lovingly at the Lion. Only then did she realise that his fur had changed to white. 'You look good,' she remarked and added, 'and so mature, like a true ruler of the Tiny Island.'

All of a sudden, the Lion looked worried.

'I am afraid that we first have to defeat the Red Firedragon, who is the transformed Capricorn. He burned me badly with his fire blasts. I was lucky that the Tigress found me in time and dragged me to the Crater Lake so I could dive in, heal and transform. I surely would have died otherwise. And the Tigress ascended to the White Dragon,' he said, sounding grateful and humble.

Just then, the Dragon put her massive head into the cave entrance to see the cubs.

'Thank you for saving Strong Lion. He means the world to me,' the Lioness addressed the Dragon.

'I think that he saved himself. He called me when he was seriously injured. I heard his call in a dream because of the old spiritual bond connecting us.

'His only thoughts were for your and the cubs' safety. He wanted me to protect you, but I knew that I could protect you only if I saved him first. I am glad that we succeeded.

'I was surprised that he managed the transformation even though he had been severely injured. But the Universal Divine Spirit must have protected him as he is still very much needed,' the White Dragon concluded.

Just as she pulled her big head out of the cave entrance, the Black Panther and the Black Jaguar appeared. When the Jaguar was about to attack the Dragon, the Panther stopped him.

'Is that you, White Tigress? You are so huge, and you look so different. But now that I see your beautiful green eyes, I know that it must be you. Is this your final stage of transformation?' the Panther asked, looking a little intimidated.

The White Dragon simply nodded.

After his initial surprise, the Panther returned quickly to the facts.

'The Red Firedragon and a giant army are fast

approaching the Great Waterhole. They are many, and we have to prepare. We cannot underestimate them,' he added.

As he spoke, the Lion came out of the cave. Although he emerged with a big grin, he immediately sensed that danger was looming when he saw the seriousness in the Panther's eyes.

'The Young Lioness and the cubs are in great danger; we all are,' the Panther addressed the Lion and the others. 'The enemy is fast approaching and outnumbers us considerably. And even though we now have the White Dragon by our side, we have to develop a plan to defeat them.'

The friends who had gathered around the Great Waterhole to fight the Red Firedragon and his followers knew that they would be fighting for their lives. The opposing army was large, aggressive and determined to be victorious.

If they were defeated, the Firedragon would spare no one unless they bent to his will. The fate of the Tiny Island depended on the White Dragon, the White Lion, the Black Panther and his friends.

They knew that they had to come up with a solid plan to overpower the enemy. As they did not have much time, they sat down and strategised how they would have to approach the task.

It helped that the Panther, the Jaguar and their friends were experienced warriors. But the others also had brave hearts, and they would fight to the death to protect their loved ones.

All of a sudden, the Dragon realised that she had not seen the Wise Cat in the cave.

'Where is the Wise Cat?' she asked. She had hoped to talk to her because she had predicted the Tigress' final transformation. Maybe the Wise Cat knew things that would be helpful for her to know before she began to fight. The Dragon had an instant urge to find the Wise Cat before the opposing army's arrival as she had the feeling that she had powers within her that were still hidden.

The Black Panther seemed to guess her thoughts.

'The Wise Cat has gone to the West coast. She is looking for friends who can support us. She must have already sensed that the newly transformed Firedragon would collect animals behind him and march against us to secure his reign,' he replied.

'After the Lioness gave birth to her cubs, the Wise Cat left; she seemed in a hurry. She said that she would look for the Grey Wolf, the Brown Bear and the Big Panda to support us. Maybe she could also convince other old friends, such as the caracals, the servals and the wild cats to help us. The Wise Cat also had a message for you, White Dragon.

'Upon your arrival, I should have told you that she was convinced that you would be successful in your next transformation. I should have let you know that you can protect the animals around you in a fight with your fire.

'She said that you would have the ability not only to breathe fire but also to produce ice if you took water into your mouth and concentrated on making frost. I did not exactly know what she meant at that moment because she did not tell me which animal you would transform into, even though I asked her. But now I understand. She seems to have foreseen that you would transform into a dragon,' the Black Panther concluded.

'I tried breathing fire, and a white blast came out. But I did not know that I could also spit frost,' the Dragon replied. She was fascinated by this thought as she knew ice from her life in the White Mountains. She could not wait to try it out.

The Panther saw how excited she was. He sensed that she wanted to fly immediately to the lake in order to practise, but he stopped her.

'Wait a moment!' he said. 'It is imperative you are here for the planning of our battle strategy. You will have to play a central role in it. May I asked you to practise the spitting of frost later?'

She looked surprised at his courage in giving her orders. But as the White Dragon, she was wiser than the Tigress and did not oppose the Panther in words or actions. She simply smiled at him, sat down patiently and waited for his instructions.

Deep down, she was impressed at how strong and determined a leader the Panther was. He obviously had so much experience in commanding his troops. He also did not shy away from leading larger animals, like the Black Jaguar, and more aggressive animals, such as the Desert Leopard.

The Panther gave instructions to the Yellow Cheetah, and within a few moments, she came back with the rest of the predators who had previously been patrolling around the Great Waterhole. Patiently, they all sat down and listened to the plan that he had formulated.

'We cannot meet the Firedragon's army directly here at the Great Waterhole. With the lake behind us, we would have no space to manoeuvre. The enemy would push us into the Great Waterhole.

'There is nowhere near where we can fight from above, and there is no narrow canyon in which we can welcome them. Even though I do not like it, we have to encounter them in the open savannah. I think we should fight them using the following strategy,' the Panther said and rolled some stones in the sand to show the others how to attack the enemy. Then he continued to outline his plan.

'The White Dragon will go in the first row. She will be flanked by the Lion and me. On our left side, the Jaguar will lead a small group of black panthers.

'The Yellow Cheetah will lead the group of cheetahs to our right. I suggest that the White Cheetah joins her,' the Panther said and smiled at the Cheetah.

Addressing the Desert Leopard, the Panther commanded, 'Lead a group of leopards and wild dogs to the edge of the savannah, where the dogs should dig several deep holes. We will lie in those holes, and you will cover the holes with branches and grass so that the enemy's army cannot see us.

'Three leopards must remain at the Great Waterhole and continue to patrol around the lake so that the Black Plague does not spread while we are fighting. We simply cannot risk that happening as all our endeavours will have been in vain. Collect your troops and start now!'

The Desert Leopard left to fulfil his task while the Panther continued to instruct the others.

'Our friends the gorillas have promised to help us as well. The Red Fody came back and told me that they are on their way to the Great Waterhole. The gorillas have to move carefully, however, so that they are not caught by the opposing army before the fight starts.

'The Wise Cat has already left and is trying to find her friends and other animals to support us, but I do not know how many will come and whether they will reach us in time. For now, we cannot count on them. The animals who are already here are pretty much all that we have for now. So we will have to work with those numbers.

'The Red Fody has told me that we are far outnumbered by the Firedragon's troops. On her way back from the gorillas, she flew over the opposing army. She was almost caught and taken down by the Black Falcon, but at the last moment she managed to hide in a Flame Tree. Although the Falcon watched the tree as he wanted to catch her, she was able to sneak out. When she chirped, the Giant Eagle came to help her and killed him.

'I hope that the Red Firedragon has not realised that we await him because the Falcon did not come back. We will have to be cautious but also brave as we do not know what he is planning. Our only chance is if he is so convinced that he will win that he lowers his guard,' the Panther added, concluding his speech.

The White Dragon knew that the plan was simple. It did not contain a lot of strategy, but the truth was that there were not many options, and no other option was viable. She did not know what he was planning with the holes, but the Panther's friends seemed to know.

She decided not to ask as she trusted his strategy. He seemed to know what he was doing. She agreed that they had only two options for where to encounter the opposing army—either close to the lake or in the savannah.

The savannah was definitely the better option. They were hugely outnumbered, and although they were all brave fighters, the fight would surely cost lives on both sides.

The White Dragon had never seen the Panther and his friends fighting before, apart from her encounter with him at the Great Waterhole. From his stories, she suspected that they could be victorious.

She was not sure how much strength she would have as the White Dragon. Her new animal body still felt unfamiliar, but she was much stronger than before, although slow and heavy. She was calm but also sad that she had to fight as she felt absolutely no aggression inside her—no hate, no anger, just pure light. And she did not want to use this light to kill other animals.

The White Dragon no longer hunted. Whenever she was hungry, she went to a tree and ate the leaves and branches. She did not eat much, though, since she gained part of the energy that she needed from the bright sunlight. The White Tigress had hunted mostly fish to still her hunger, but the White Dragon no longer had this urge. It was as if the former empress of the Asantian rainforest had become a giant, peaceful guardian of the light.

A battle was the last thing that she desired, and yet it was inevitable. All she wanted was peace. It saddened her heart that there was no other way than to either fight or perish—and with her all the good animals on the Tiny Island.

She had to fight for Young Leo. She wanted to fight for the White Cheetah, Young Cham, the lion family and also for the Black Panther, although she knew that he was more than capable of fighting for himself.

All animals on the Tiny Island had the right to live in freedom. However, this freedom was endangered by the Red Firedragon. The White Dragon knew that he had to be stopped, and she would fight with her life to defeat him.

CHAPTER TWENTY-THREE

Preparations

'They are coming, they are coming!' the Fody chirped. The White Dragon could sense the fear in her voice.

The Red Fody and the Giant Eagle had been given the task of flying deep into the savannah and reporting back when and from which direction the Firedragon's army was approaching. They had to make sure that they did not get too close to the enemy, to avoid being caught by the flying scouts. Although they had encountered the Black Falcon, they had managed to avoid the grey vultures.

They had brought back the news that the enemy would arrive shortly after sunset.

'We have to start preparing instantly,' the Panther said. 'I assume they will sleep in the savannah and fight us at the first sunlight. I doubt that they will attack earlier as they will be too tired from their march. They will need to eat to regain their strength. They are not familiar with the territory and cannot be sure what we have prepared for them,' he explained.

Everyone nodded. The Panther was content. It was always better if the troops were convinced that the strategy of their commander would lead to victory, he thought.

'White Dragon, you have to go to the lake and smear your scales with mud. They shine too brightly in the sunlight, as well as in the moonlight.

'The same applies to all other white and yellow animals. You all have to smear yourself with mud so that no one can distinguish you from the soil.

'We cannot risk being spotted. The black animals should do this as well—just to be sure,' the Panther told them.

Once he had given the instruction, the friends went to the lake shore and rolled in the mud. The White Cheetah hesitated, but she did as she had been told when she saw that the White Dragon was following the Panther's directions.

'Do you know why we have to do this?' the Cheetah asked the Dragon as she felt uncomfortable smudging her beautiful white fur.

'I think it is because the Panther wants us to camouflage ourselves. And if we smell of soil, they cannot trace us. Maybe that is why he ordered the black animals to roll in the mud as well. Can you please smear some mud on my wings?' the White Dragon asked the now-not-so-White Cheetah, who laughed her typical cheetah laugh.

The Dragon laughed, too, as it looked so funny when the Cheetah rolled herself in the dirt. Amid all the serious preparations for the battle, this was their release.

When they were finished, they looked more like rocks made of mud than animals.

'The mud will prevent the enemy's army not only from seeing us, but also from smelling us,' the Panther explained, confirming the explanation that the White Dragon had given to the Cheetah.

'We will now make our way to the holes that the wild dogs have dug in the savannah. There we will hide until we can attack.

'Once night approaches and the animals in the Firedragon's camp are asleep, we will charge forward. That is our only chance,' the Panther insisted.

'With a touch of luck or destiny—whichever way you see it—the enemy's army will rest close to our holes and we will be able to sneak up on them without being seen by their night guards. We can win only if we surprise them in their sleep; otherwise, our chances are minimal.

'If we can get hold of the Red Firedragon early in the battle and kill him, that will hopefully convince his army to give up. They will have put their faith in his black magic, and without his leadership, they will be lost. The Fody told me that his army includes many predators. However, I am more worried about the poisonous snakes,' he concluded.

'He looks like a worried rock made of mud,' the Cheetah murmured.

The White Dragon had to admit that the Panther's plan was far from simple. It made sense, although she did not like the idea that they had to attack first. He was right that this was their only chance of getting hold of the Red Firedragon early in the fight.

The Dragon hoped that it would end the battle immediately. She also agreed that it made sense for her to be in the front row. Equally, the Black Panther had to be in the front, as one could not lead from behind.

'I will join the Jaguar, not the Yellow Cheetah. I think that his fighters may need my support because I am very fast,' the White Cheetah proclaimed suddenly.

'I agree. That is a brilliant idea. We need a fast runner on the right flank,' concurred the Jaguar before anyone could say anything.

The Dragon could see that the Jaguar was happy that he would be able to protect the White Cheetah. It was apparent to anyone who was not completely blind that the two had fallen deeply in love.

'So be it,' the Panther said. He did not want to get into an argument with the Jaguar shortly before the battle as he understood instinctively that the animals protected those they loved.

The predators started to move towards the savannah. They had to move slowly as they did not want to shake the dirt from their bodies.

In the late afternoon, they reached the savannah. The friends lay flat in the holes that the wild dogs had dug for them. Then the leopards brought tree branches to cover the holes and the wild dogs pushed clumps of grass over the branches so that they could not be distinguished from the surroundings.

They had to make the hole for the White Dragon extra big so that she could fit inside. Left and right from the Dragon were the holes for the Lion and the Panther.

The Jaguar, the White Cheetah and a few panthers squeezed themselves into holes on the left side, and the other cheetahs took their places in holes on the right.

'Now walk along the lake and hide with your troops so that you can enter the battle from behind once you hear the cry of the Giant Eagle,' the Panther instructed the Desert Leopard.

Everyone was ready and eager to leave the holes as soon as possible, but they knew that they would have to be patient and wait for the Panther's sign for them to charge forward.

When the enemy slept, the Panther wanted to send the Fody from his hole into the sky, where the Giant Eagle was already waiting.

After his signal, the Eagle would make a noise and the animals would sneak out of their holes, trying to instantly overpower the Red Firedragon so that further bloodshed was avoided.

As she sat in her pit, the White Dragon realised that it might be hours before the opposing army arrived. She had to be patient and focus on the battle ahead. She remembered her meditations with the Golden Hare.

She calmed her mind and focused on her breath. During the meditation, she reached the state of awareness and alertness that she needed. She let her thoughts come and go and embraced for the first time her new animal spirit and her body as the White Dragon.

She discovered that her power centre was her heart and understood that she had to be one with the Universal Divine Spirit to defeat the Red Firedragon.

She concentrated on herself and the upcoming battle and entered into a meditative state in which she actively felt her surroundings.

At the same time, she was able to focus her consciousness on a level that went beyond the material world.

All of a sudden, the White Dragon felt the spirits of the animals surrounding her. She could sense their fears, anger, love and determination. Her spirit experienced the various emotions of those animals. She let them pass by and acknowledged them without judging.

She realised that it was her destiny to fight the Red Firedragon in order to save the animals of the Tiny Island. She felt that she had to manifest her victory for it to become reality. She smiled and then opened her eyes slowly.

It was now shortly before sunset. Suddenly, the White Dragon heard the distant noise of hundreds of stamping hooves, paws and claws, and she knew that the enemy's army was fast approaching.

She understood that she had to lie still from that moment on. She focused her thoughts again and reached out to the Panther's spirit. He was in a hole to her right, not far from her. She sensed that he was calm but alert. She knew that he had been trained for battle ever since joining the fight against the cruel Lion Brothers.

Then her focus shifted to the White Lion. His feelings were the exact opposite. She felt his rage and anger towards his stepfather. She also felt his anxiety and could sense that he was overwhelmed. His whole concern was now for his three cubs.

The White Dragon feared that all those emotions might cloud his judgement. She doubted that he would be able to focus on the coming fight. Instead, his recklessness and anger might overpower his rational brain. She hoped that the Lion would calm down, but she decided that she could do nothing about it at that moment and no longer worried about his struggles. She had reached a state of detachment from this world that prepared her for the battle.

Then her focus shifted to the coming fight with the Red Firedragon. She knew if she defeated him, further bloodshed could be avoided.

Suddenly, she sensed his animal spirit. His energy was raw, violent and consumed by evil. He would show neither mercy nor forgiveness nor remorse. For a moment, she had tapped into his energy and had felt only hate and wrath for all living creatures.

The White Dragon experienced a deep sense of disgust, but at the same time, she was overwhelmed by feelings of sadness and pity—sadness that his spirit was thoroughly evil, and pity that his spirit had lost even the slightest glimmer of light.

She at once pulled back her animal spirit, not knowing whether the Red Firedragon was now aware that another dragon was out there, ready to fight him. Did he understand who was awaiting him? Did he recognise that she was the former White Tigress? Did he know where she was and what they had planned?

The White Dragon was still insecure about her newly acquired abilities, and she reached out to the Panther's spirit. Maybe it was silly for her, as a strong and determined White Dragon, to have feelings of uncertainty, but she did not care.

Deep down, she understood that she had to touch his spirit once again before the great battle. He sensed her insecurity, but meeting his spirit comforted her greatly. She breathed in and out deeply and now understood that events would turn out as the Universal Divine Spirit had planned them aeons ago.

Her thoughts were interrupted by noises not far from them. The Firedragon's army must have come to a halt and seems to be settling down for the night, exactly as the Black Panther anticipated, she acknowledged. After a while, the noises from the enemy's camp died down and she could hear the breathing of numerous animals in the otherwise silent savannah.

When the White Dragon heard the cry of the Giant Eagle, she knew it was time to approach the camp. Although they had hoped that the Firedragon's army would come to a halt directly in front of them, that was not the case. They would have to run some distance before they reached the enemy.

Maybe this was the best outcome, she thought. Otherwise we might have been discovered by the guards before we could attack them.

The White Dragon lifted her huge body out of the hole as silently as possible. She could not see much, but she quickly realised that the others had already charged towards the opponent's camp.

She tried out her wings, which were covered in mud. What a stupid idea to put dirt on my wings, she thought. I must have been out of my mind. She had to shake her wings a few times before the mud flew off.

The White Dragon started flying, but with the mud on the rest of her body, it was far more difficult than she had anticipated. As she took off, she saw fire coming from the night sky that set the dry grass of the savannah alight. Immediately, a second blast of fire shot down from the sky. She heard screams and roars. The battle had begun.

CHAPTER TWENTY-FOUR

The Battle

The fight was already in full swing as the White Dragon flew to the battlefield. The friends fought the elephants, who stampeded through the grass and sought to stab them with their tusks. The poisonous snakes tried to bite them, and the buffalos and rhinos used their horns to pierce every animal who was not fast enough to escape.

Although the friends were far outnumbered, one fought for ten. They absolutely had the strength and the agility to withstand the enemy.

Fighting had become second nature to the Black Panther and his troops because for a long time they had combatted the Lion Brothers in Avaria. But the others, too, were courageous and determined.

The White Lion searched the battleground. He was disappointed not to find the Red Firedragon. In contrast, the Firedragon saw him from above. He swiftly concluded that this could only be his stepson and that he had transformed as well. He was surprised that the Lion was not already dead, but he vowed that he soon would be.

The Firedragon breathed fire towards the White Lion, hitting him on his tail. The Lion roared in

pain, but he did not think about giving up. Instead, he plunged into the fray and, together with the Black Jaguar, took down one of the elephants.

When the White Dragon had almost reached the battlefield, she again saw fire light up the night sky. She heard a roar from the Yellow Cheetah, who had been directly hit by the blast.

Then, out of nowhere, she heard the sound of wings nearby. The Firedragon had discovered her presence, and he swiftly breathed fire at her. Yet her scaled skin was not burned; it only started to glow in the night— repelling his fire.

The Red Firedragon was now close enough to see the White Dragon properly for the first time. He immediately grasped that he was fighting against the transformed Tigress. His evil eyes were full of hate.

The two dragons collided in the air, drilling their claws and teeth deeply into each other's flesh. They fell from the sky, and their intertwined bodies rolled across the ground. Instantly, they bit and clawed each other. There was, however, a balance between them; neither could gain an advantage.

In the meantime, the battle in the savannah continued. Even though the friends fought bravely, they lost ground. Two leopards were already dead, and the Yellow Cheetah was severely wounded. The Panther dragged her to a nearby Flame Tree, ordered one of the friends to protect her and went back to the battleground.

At the same time, the Jaguar, the Desert Leopard and the White Cheetah were attacking another elephant, who had killed the two leopards. When the Panther went to help them, they jointly took down the raging elephant.

Suddenly, the Desert Leopard screamed. While fighting the elephant, he had not noticed that three cobras had surrounded him. The moment the predators killed the elephant, the cobras attacked the Leopard.

Although the Jaguar came quickly to his aid and tore the snakes in two, the Leopard had been bitten multiple times and passed out.

The Jaguar dragged him to a Flame Tree and tried to suck the poison out of his body, but there were just too many bites. The Desert Leopard remained unconscious, and the Jaguar instinctively knew that he would soon lose his friend, who was breathing shallowly. But he had to return to the battleground to aid the others. Meanwhile, the Panther was fighting off a black rhino. He jumped on the rhino's back and killed him with one bite to his neck.

While the White Dragon was fighting the Red Firedragon, they were suddenly surrounded by numerous wolves and four crocodiles. It was as if the Firedragon had called them telepathically.

They formed a circle around the two dragons and charged towards the White Dragon. Although her skin had withstood the fire, it could not withstand their bites. It would only be a matter of time before they defeated her.

The White Dragon calmly reached out to the Black Panther and the White Lion to call for help. She touched both of their spirits at once.

However, when she realised that the fight on the battlefield had turned in favour of the opposing army, she immediately pulled back and refocused her energy on withstanding the enemy.

With renewed determination, she shook off the wolves, but the crocodiles attacked her legs so that she stumbled and fell.

Instantly, the Firedragon attacked. He bit her neck and sank his teeth deep into her flesh. The White Dragon roared in pain. Her mind turned from the fight to Young Leo. She had to fight for him; she simply could not be defeated.

Out of nowhere, the White Lion and the Black Panther appeared by her side and fought off the crocodiles. The White Dragon stood up and breathed white fire towards the Firedragon. It burned his skin, while her skin seemed to repel his blasts without taking much damage. The Red Firedragon roared in pain and took off, flying in the direction of the Great Waterhole.

'The Firedragon is heading towards the cave where the Young Lioness is hiding with our cubs. I felt him touching my mind, and although I resisted, he must have found out where she is and that she has given birth. I need to save them because he wants to take revenge by killing them,' the Lion roared and ran towards the cave to save the Young Lioness and their cubs.

After the White Dragon and the Panther had finally defeated the wolves and crocodiles, they both returned to the main battlefield. There, the situation was dire.

Even though their friends had killed many animals from the opposing army, they had suffered great losses. Most of the black panthers and cheetahs were dead after being bitten by the cobras or trampled under the hooves of the rhinos.

When they reached the battleground, only the White Cheetah, the Black Jaguar and the Snow Leopard remained, standing back to back in a circle, defending themselves against the approaching enemies.

'We need to join them inside the circle at once; otherwise, we will all die,' the Panther shouted to the Dragon.

'There are still numerous animals fighting on the enemy's side. We will be overpowered soon unless a miracle happens,' the White Cheetah roared, full of desperation. The Dragon could sense that she was afraid that she would never see Young Cham again.

'We can still hold out for a while,' the Panther replied to calm the Cheetah.

The White Dragon knew that the Panther would never give up. She reached out her mind into the savannah and sensed that the gorillas would arrive soon. Then her animal spirit met the Wise Cat's spirit. She felt her optimism and understood that support would also come from that side.

'The gorillas will arrive soon. We need to stand strong until they arrive. The Wise Cat will also bring help. Do not give up, my friends!' the White Dragon roared.

More than three dozen gorillas charged directly towards the circle of friends. They were running fast, and they cut a swathe through the enemy's ranks, fighting with their paws, teeth and heads. It was like a stampede over the smaller animals of the Firedragon's army.

When they reached the friends, they formed an outer circle around the five exhausted predators who were still left. The gorillas fought off rhinos, wolves and crocodiles with their bare paws.

'I am so glad that you are here,' the Cheetah said. 'We would not have been able to hold off the enemy much longer.'

'We can keep them busy for a while, but we need more support,' the commander of the gorillas, an experienced silverback, replied. 'Are these all of your troops who are left?' he asked with concern, while boxing an approaching wolf in the head.

'For now, this is all that we have. So we need to make it count. I suggest that you draw one or two rhinos or crocodiles into the inner circle, and then we will kill them,' the Panther commanded. 'Fly up into the air and try to use your white fire to fight the enemy,' he directed the White Dragon.

Although she did not like to be given orders, she flew up into the air to breathe fire from above. She understood that she was better suited to fighting in the air than on the ground after the arrival of the gorillas. With her transformation from the Tigress to the Dragon, she had left her ego behind. All that she wanted was to end the battle.

Before she could breathe fire even once, her animal spirit felt a call. The Lion was struggling to defend the Young Lioness and their cubs against the Red Firedragon. He urgently needed help.

The White Dragon instantly flew over to the Panther's cave. Even though it was imperative for her to remain close to the battleground, she understood that the Lion was the future ruler of the Tiny Island and that he would be very much needed once the Firedragon had been defeated. She already knew that the Wise Cat would arrive soon with further help.

The cave was not far away, so she reached it quickly.

CHAPTER TWENTY-FIVE

Saving the White Lion

The White Dragon witnessed a peculiar scene at the Panther's cave. As the Firedragon was too large to pass through the narrow entrance, he had put only his big head into the cave to breathe fire towards the lions. Inside, the Lion was trying to protect the Young Lioness and their cubs from the blasts.

The White Dragon anticipated that the lion family would already have retreated to the back of the cave, thereby avoiding the intensity of the flames. The air, however, would not last much longer, as every fire blast reduced the oxygen inside, slowly suffocating the lions.

She knew that she had to act quickly. Without further thought, she sank her teeth into the tail of the Firedragon and dragged him out of the cave entrance with one pull. She was in her full power. She finally understood the guidance of the Golden Hare and was in complete alignment with her destiny.

With incredible willpower, the Firedragon managed to shake off the White Dragon. Now they stood facing each other. He, too, was fully focused and aware of himself and in alignment with his destiny.

The White Dragon realised that both good and

evil could be in perfect alignment because they were opposing forces—and the events were fated although their outcome was open.

The Red Firedragon lost no time in breathing fire at her. She matched his red fire with her white fire. The blasts met and cancelled each other out. Their forces were equally balanced.

At that moment, the two lions came out of the Panther's cave, carrying the three cubs in their mouths. The White Lion's fur was severely burned from protecting his family.

Luckily, the Firedragon did not see them coming out of the entrance as he was focused on fighting the White Dragon. The lions retreated quickly from the dragons' battleground and hid themselves and their cubs.

The White Dragon sincerely hoped that they would stay out of sight and that the Lion would not re-enter the battle between the dragons. She could not risk him dying in the course of the fight. He had to survive for his family. But she was familiar with his reckless nature, his pride and ego. Although he had matured considerably, these attributes still formed part of his character.

She should have known from the teachings of the Hare not to manifest negative thoughts as they would inevitably lead to negative events.

The Lion showed up only moments later, ready to enter the fight and prepared to claim victory with the White Dragon. He jumped on the back of the Firedragon and bit deeply into his neck while the two dragons breathed fire at each other. The Firedragon immediately flew high into the sky to shake off the

Lion. At the same time, he breathed fire from above towards the White Dragon, who deflected his attack.

The White Dragon also flew into the air so that she was again on the same level as him. Although she was able to absorb his fire with her glow, she decided to fly towards the lake, anticipating that the Red Firedragon would follow her.

She feared that the Lion would soon fall off the Firedragon's back, land on the ground and die as both dragons were fighting high in the sky. The Lion's only chance of survival would be to fall into the Great Waterhole.

When the White Dragon reached the lake, she turned around and breathed fire towards the Red Firedragon, with her fire hitting his head so that he tumbled backwards. The Firedragon managed to stay in the air, but the Lion fell off his back into the lake. He was saved and swam to the shore.

The two dragons continued their fire-fight, but neither of them could gain an advantage. Both dragons knew that they would have to enter into close combat to defeat the other, but they did not give up their stalemate position.

Then something unexpected happened. The White Dragon noticed that her breath of white fire had become weak and that the Firedragon's breath had also become frail. She understood at once that constantly breathing fire at each other must have made the fire weaker. Both dragons would soon lose their firepower, and they would have to pause.

The White Dragon sensed that the moment for close combat had come. With a loud yell, she rammed into the Red Firedragon, and they dug their teeth and claws into each other's bodies. They could not maintain their position in the air and fell into the deep waters of the Great Waterhole.

There, the two creatures broke away from each other, and the White Dragon sucked in water through her mouth. Although she could not breathe underwater, her intuition told her to suck in a substantial amount of water.

Meanwhile, the Red Firedragon had already made his way out of the lake. He rose again into the sky, waiting to attack her the moment that she broke the surface. With regained energy, he breathed fire towards her.

When the White Dragon reached the water's surface and shot up into the sky, she spat out frost from the water that she had drawn in instead of her white fire.

When the fire and ice met, they cancelled each other out and became hot steam. The two dragons could no longer see.

That was the moment when the White Dragon followed her intuition and charged through the mist, heading directly towards the Red Firedragon, who seemed confused by the sudden turn of events.

She rammed her big horned head into the puzzled Firedragon, who lost his balance and fell onto the shore of the lake. Immediately, the White Dragon breathed fire at him, burning his skin.

She sensed that with a couple more attacks he would be defeated. She felt pity for him. Maybe there was still light in his spirit and he could be saved. She questioned the necessity of killing him.

But she did not have the chance to pursue this line of thought. Running out from behind a Flame Tree nearby, the White Lion attacked the Firedragon, who was lying in the gravel on the lake shore, and bit him in the neck.

Even though the Firedragon was severely wounded, he quickly flew into the sky and breathed fire at the Lion on the ground, hitting him directly on the head. The Lion roared in pain.

The White Dragon sent a last breath of fire towards the Firedragon, who fled in the direction of the extinct volcano. She could not follow him as she had to take care of the Lion, who was badly injured.

'Young Lioness, please come and help me. The White Lion is seriously wounded. We have to put water on his skin to cool his burns,' the White Dragon roared into the sky, hoping that the Lioness would hear her cry. However, the Lion had taken his family far away from the dragons' battleground so that they would be safe.

The White Dragon swiftly flew to the lake, sucked in water and poured it onto the Lion's burned skin. She could not use her breath of frost as it would have killed him.

This time around, things did not look too good for the Lion. He will die, she thought.

The Dragon sent this thought into the universe, where she instantly connected with the Wise Cat, who already knew that the Lion had been severely wounded, as she had a deep spiritual connection with her stepson.

Help is coming soon, the Wise Cat's voice echoed in the mind of the Dragon, who gently laid her claw on the body of the Lion as he was breathing only shallowly.

CHAPTER TWENTY-SIX

The Red Firedragon's Fate

T he White Dragon looked into the sky and saw a strange creature. As it came closer, she realised that it was a giant balloon made of water lily leaves.

A basket fashioned out of banyan tree branches was hanging under the balloon.

The Brown Bear and other animals sat in the basket while they headed directly towards her. The Brown Bear has finally made his dream come true and invented an airship, the Dragon thought.

When the balloon landed, the Wise Cat jumped out first and ran straight to the wounded Lion. She immediately started the healing procedure, applying several potions to his wounds and burns.

Meanwhile, the Brown Bear tied the balloon to a Flame Tree with strong vines. The other animals got out of the basket, among them the Big Panda, the Grey Wolf, three wild cats and several caracals. The Wise Cat had managed to convince these animals to help them in their fight against the Firedragon's army.

'You have to go quickly and support our friends on the battleground. They are fighting bravely, but they urgently need help as the enemy is strong,' the White Dragon addressed the newcomers. 'I will follow the Firedragon, who just left the Great Waterhole. He was wounded and flew in the direction of the extinct volcano. He can no longer harm you on the battlefield. I will fly to the crater and either make him surrender or kill him.'

The animals heard the determination in her voice and followed her orders. They charged towards the savannah, where the friends were still fighting the opposing army.

'Will the Lion survive?' the Dragon asked the Wise Cat. She was worried about him and his young family.

'I have done my best with my healing potions, and I have also used white magic to heal him. Now it is up to the Universal Divine Spirit to save him. I will look for the Young Lioness and their cubs and bring them to be with him. Maybe the miracle of life of his new-born cubs will save him.

'White Dragon, go now. The safety of the Tiny Island depends on you. You will need to fight the Red Firedragon. It is your destiny. You were born for this fight; you were born to save the Tiny Island.

'Please take this magic potion. If you feel that the task is impossible, put three drops of the potion on something that can help you with your quest, and you will see things become possible that were impossible before.

'Also take these four magic balls that I made from the skin of a dead elephant and these two grey stones. As you already know, you can use them to walk underwater. The grey stone will take you to the bottom of any water body, the blue ball will give you fresh air underwater, and the green ball will bring you up again.

'I will give you two of each because you may need help. I had a vision that you will need to go to the bottom of the Crater Lake to save the Tiny Island. The lake is deep, but with the help of my magic balls and stones, you will manage.

'Always remember, even if the task seems impossible, it will be possible. The Universal Divine Spirit will always give you a challenge that seems difficult at first but is not impossible to complete. He will not give you more than you can handle in your current state of being, but also not less.

'Destiny is destiny because it can go either way—it can go in your favour or against you. If we were not challenged, we would never grow or transform. Either the good or the evil may win; otherwise, the scales would not be balanced. The Universal Divine Spirit always seeks equilibrium. Go now. Go! Meet your destiny!' the Wise Cat urged the Dragon, who thanked her and said a brief goodbye. She knew that the Wise Cat had insight into the divine—that she knew much more than the White Dragon herself and had visions of the future. So she did not ask any questions.

Sunset was fast approaching, and the White Dragon would reach the area around the crater only as night fell. She flew directly to the extinct volcano, where she hoped to encounter the Red Firedragon, as she was sure that he would be waiting for her there. The Firedragon had had enough time to heal his wounds and would be ready to fight her.

When she arrived at the foot of the volcano, she could not see him, even though the full moon was shining brightly. Then she flew upwards to the Crater Lake, hoping to find him there. But there, too, she could not spot him. She was at a loss.

Then she remembered the words of the Golden Hare: that facing uncertain situations and deciding a course of action required great focus. She stood still and began to direct her animal spirit towards the events to come.

She felt her spirit intensely, but she also experienced her current body and mind as the White Dragon.

Past, present and future merged into one at that moment. Her transformations now made complete sense to her.

The losses, heartbreaks and betrayals had prepared her for this one coming fight. She felt that those adversities had not made her heart bitter; on the contrary, her heart had become warmer. She had become more loving, caring and trusting towards other animals, for she saw not only the darkness but also the light in them.

Although she would have to fight the Red Firedragon fiercely, she knew that only her love for all living beings on the Tiny Island would bring her victory. She felt blessed, one with the world, whole as an animal spirit and in alignment with the Universal Divine Spirit. She was ready not only for the fight with the Firedragon but also to meet her destiny.

Her destiny came from high in the night sky and greeted her with a breath of red fire. The White Dragon answered it with a blast of her white fire. The two fire blasts met.

The White Dragon could feel that the intensity of the Firedragon's fire had increased. She did not care. She was in her power; she was in alignment with her internal source energy, which was as powerful as her destiny.

Her intense white fire surprised the Red Firedragon, who had expected an easy win over the White Dragon, given that he had not only healed himself but also increased the strength of his fire with black magic.

Both dragons seemed to be tapping into an infinite

power source. Even though they fought each other for some time, their fire was not becoming weaker.

The moon had set, but the dragons could still see each other. More importantly, they felt each other's spirit. The fight between them was a fight not only in the physical realm but also between animal spirits—a battle between good and evil, a battle between light, on one side, and pride, hatred and ego, on the other.

The White Dragon charged forward blasting white fire. The Red Firedragon initially lost ground but did not give up. He had used black magic to shield his skin against her fire and applied poisonous potions to protect him in close combat.

He wanted to make it impossible for her to bite or dig her claws into his skin without being poisoned. Although the White Dragon did not know about the poison that protected his skin, she sensed that she had to change her tactics to defeat him.

The White Dragon paused for a moment. Before she continued blasting white fire at the Firedragon, she reached out one more time to his animal spirit, as she believed that there might still be a trace of good in him.

She did not want to lose the opportunity that he might voluntarily surrender because he had understood that evil was not the solution.

When her spirit reached out to his, he displayed no resistance. It was almost as if he was welcoming her in. She searched in his animal spirit, and like the last time their two spirits had met, she could find only darkness and evil. He had surrendered to the evil.

Not even a tiny flicker of light shone inside him. All she could feel was the determination to defeat her and then spread hate, hopelessness and despair across the Tiny Island.

The White Dragon was disappointed, but she had to refocus her mind on the fight in the physical realm.

The Red Firedragon took advantage of her short distraction to fly high into the sky above the shore of the Crater Lake, ready to swoop down and kill her.

Perhaps he expected her to fly up to engage him in close combat and bite him so that the strong poison on his skin would weaken her. He knew that the Tigress would not have shied away from attacking him.

But the transformed White Dragon did not move at all. She remained on the ground and focused her mind on her internal source energy, just as she had learned to do from the Golden Hare.

She surrendered to the guidance of her animal spirit, feeling that it was the right thing to do. Whereas the Tigress had remained tied to her physical existence, the White Dragon was not.

Like a ball of fire hurtling from the sky, the Red Firedragon fell headfirst towards the White Dragon. He aimed to crash into her back, hoping that he would defeat her by the sheer impact of his massive body plummeting from the sky.

Although his fire could not damage her skin, as her glow protected her, his massive head could crush her back or even her skull.

Still the White Dragon did not move.

The Red Firedragon was now confident that he would defeat her. Just as he was about to ram into her, she danced aside. He could not stop his approach, and his head crashed directly into the gravel surrounding the Crater Lake.

He was stuck. Fountains of blood gushed from his head. The White Dragon knew that his injuries were critical and that he would die soon. She did not feel any joy about his defeat, just sadness that his animal spirit had followed the path of darkness.

But the Firedragon was not finished yet. He pulled his head out of the gravel and used his remaining energy to fly back high into the sky. Then he fell directly into the Crater Lake and vanished into the floods.

The White Dragon was surprised. What was he hoping to achieve by diving into the Crater Lake? Did he expect to transform again? She assumed that he had already reached his final stage of transformation—but one could never be sure.

At that moment, the White Dragon felt the earth move, and she saw three fountains of fire rising out of the Crater Lake—two thin ones, and one thicker.

Were those fire blasts from the Firedragon's nostrils and mouth? But then she realised that the three fountains of fire coming out of the Crater Lake consisted of heated red soil.

She had seen such fountains as a cub in the Asantian rainforest. One of the active volcanos nearby had erupted, and she and her family had had to run for their lives as melted stones, which the elders called lava, flowed from the volcano's crater and destroyed a large part of the rainforest.

She remembered how scared they all had been and how lucky they had been to lose only their home in that disaster, not their lives.

The White Dragon recognised that the three fountains of fire would continue, and the Tiny Island would soon be destroyed, unless she took action.

The Firedragon's last act had been targeted at destroying the Tiny Island by activating the extinct volcano.

The White Dragon did not know how he had managed to reanimate the volcano, but she expected that he had used his black magic skills one last time to do so.

CHAPTER TWENTY-SEVEN

On the Battleground

While the two dragons were fighting, the situation on the battlefield had become more serious for the remaining friends as they had lost ground against the opposing army.

Even though they were fighting bravely, they could not defeat the other side as they were simply outnumbered.

They had killed the hyenas and wolves on the enemy's side, but most of the gorillas, the Snow Leopard, the three wild cats and the caracals on their side had been killed. The last elephant and numerous white rhinos of the Firedragon's army had stampeded and killed most of the friends and their supporters.

Only the commanding silverback gorilla, two other silverbacks, the Black Panther, the Black Jaguar, the White Cheetah, the Brown Bear, the Big Panda and the Grey Wolf were left. They all knew that if further help did not arrive soon, they would die.

The Panther reached out to the White Dragon, hoping that she would have defeated the Firedragon by now, but he could not connect to her as her animal spirit was closed off.

She must still be fighting him, he thought. He was sure that he would have felt it if she had died. He

sincerely hoped that he would see her again, but it did not look good for them on the battlefield either.

Then something terrible happened. The remaining elephant and the white rhinos of the opposing army were fast approaching for a second stampede. The friends were standing in a single circle because there were only nine of them left to defend themselves.

As the enemy reached their circle, the Cheetah was standing on the side where the stampede hit hardest. The Jaguar, trying to protect her, pushed her aside so that she would not be trampled, but the Cheetah—not expecting his push—stumbled.

At that moment, the second wave of white rhinos approached. The Cheetah, being fully exposed to the stampede as she was already lying on the ground, would surely have died if the Jaguar had not heroically thrown himself on top of her to protect her life.

The remaining animals closed their defensive circle after the rhinos and the elephant had passed in an attempt to save both of them.

The White Cheetah was wounded but had survived. The Black Jaguar, however, was critically injured as the hooves of the rhinos had crushed his skull.

'Please do not die. I love you. Please do not die,' the Cheetah roared desperately, fervently hoping that he would survive.

But the Jaguar's head had been crushed, and he died in the paws of the Cheetah, looking into her beautiful eyes full of love for the last time.

The Black Panther was also devastated. During all their time fighting together in Avaria, the Panther had forged a strong bond with the Jaguar, who had been not only his deputy but a close friend.

The Panther knew that they would need the White Dragon immediately if they were to withstand the enemy any longer.

Again the Panther tried to connect to her animal spirit, and once more he could not reach her. It was as if she had vanished from the earth.

Just when all seemed lost, the miracle that the friends had been hoping for finally happened.

But it was not the White Dragon who came to rescue them. High in the sky, the giant balloon flew over the battlefield, with the Wise Cat sitting in the basket. She was a fearless wild cat. After tending to the wounds of the White Lion, she had quickly jumped into the balloon and taken off.

The Brown Bear had stored coconuts in the basket that could be thrown onto the heads of their enemies. While she was in the air, the Wise Cat had applied magic potions to those coconuts.

Now, in addition to being missiles, they would diffuse white smoke that would make the animals sleep. The Wise Cat just had to be careful to throw them amongst their enemies and not near their own troops.

While the friends were fighting the Firedragon's army, they saw the Wise Cat in the sky throwing coconuts from the balloon. When she tossed them, fine smoke drifted between the enemy's ranks, and the first animals

dropped down as if they were dead. Within a short while, dozens of them were unconscious.

The friends' hope was rekindled, although many of the animals of the opposing forces were still engaging them. Even now the Black Panther did not know whether the help of the Wise Cat would be enough.

But then something unexpected happened. Suddenly, the army of the Red Firedragon stood still. Then they retreated. Most of the fighters on the enemy's side were running away.

The Panther was confused. Should they continue to fight those animals who had given up fighting? After all, they had killed most of his friends. Or should they show mercy? His thoughts were spinning.

What he did not know was that the magic of the Firedragon had compelled those animals to fight for him. The moment he died, the spell broke, and the animals who had followed him were freed—no longer bound by his black magic.

'Look at the extinct volcano. There is fire coming out!' the White Cheetah roared, interrupting the Panther's thought process. He looked towards the volcano and saw the three fountains of fire erupting out of the volcano high into the sky. Everyone was confused.

'The volcano has been sleeping for a long time, but I think something must have awoken it. We are no longer safe here. We must head towards the North Shore and try to cross the ocean to the Hat Rock. I think we can survive there until the volcano goes to sleep again,' the Brown Bear explained. He had experienced various adventures around the world, invented countless things and gained extensive knowledge about almost everything.

All of a sudden, the Black Panther felt the White Dragon reach out to him telepathically. Her ability to communicate in this way had increased significantly since she had become a dragon.

The Red Firedragon is dead. I defeated him, but he activated the volcano, and lava is spitting out of the crater. It will surely destroy the Tiny Island if I do not stop it. The volcano needs to be quietened.

Please help to rescue the other animals from the lava, which will soon cover the soil of the entire Tiny Island.

Tell Young Leo that I love him and that I will come back once I have managed to stop the eruption. Please also tell him that he should help you and the White Cheetah to guide all animals to the elevated Hat Rock near the North Shore.

I think that it is the only place where everyone will be safe as there is an expanse of water between the Tiny Island and the Hat Rock, she explained to him. *Black Panther, I love you. Please always remember this.*

The Black Panther knew instinctively that she would have to risk her life to halt the eruption.

He could not accept this. She was still very much needed. She was the new guardian of the Tiny Island, and she had to be there for Young Leo, who had no one else to protect him and who was still not a fully grown lion.

The Panther understood that the idea of escaping to the Hat Rock was an excellent solution to save all animals if the lava continued to flow.

But his main priority was to stop the volcano altogether and to help the White Dragon to do so. He instructed the Cheetah and the remaining friends briefly to warn all animals and tell them that they should meet at the North Shore of the Tiny Island and make their way to the Hat Rock.

'All animals will be safe there. I need to head to the Crater Lake immediately in order to help the White Dragon stop the lava fountains,' the Panther said before leaving swiftly in the direction of the volcano.

For once, the Cheetah did not second-guess him. She understood that he wanted not only to help the White Dragon to halt the eruption but also to protect her.

The Cheetah felt that the predators who had recently come from Avaria would give their lives to protect the ones they loved. She had just lost the Black Jaguar, and although the pain had numbed her, she needed to lead all animals to the safety of the Hat Rock.

She would need the help of the Red Fody, the Giant Eagle and all her other friends to make sure that all animals went to the North Shore and crossed the patch of ocean between the Tiny Island and the Hat Rock.

CHAPTER TWENTY-EIGHT

The Challenge

When the Panther reached the foot of the volcano, he could see the lava fountains at the top shooting into the sky. He reached out telepathically to the White Dragon, expecting that she must already be at the Crater Lake.

'Black Panther, why are you here?' the Dragon asked him. But the voice was not in his head—it was coming from above. She was flying directly above him.

'I am going to help you to stop the lava. No animal, not even a dragon like you, can solve such a difficult problem alone. I felt you needed help,' he responded.

'I have not been able to find a viable solution so far!' she said, and her voice sounded desperate. 'The lava keeps shooting out of the Crater Lake, and the flow keeps getting stronger. The Red Firedragon caused the volcano to erupt by plunging down from the sky and piercing the bottom of the lake.

'The Wise Cat gave me a magic potion that I can put on something that could help me to perform a seemingly impossible task. But I honestly do not know what I should put the potion on.

'My best idea so far is to dive down and see whether I can use the potion somehow to close the holes at the bottom. The Crater Lake is growing warm, but it is not yet hot. If I do not get too close to the lava fountains, I might be able to fill the holes with sediment from the lake bed,' she explained.

The White Dragon sounded exhausted. For the first time since they had met, the Panther was seeing her in a situation in which she had no ready solution to fix the problem at hand.

His body, too, was exhausted from fighting and then racing towards the crater. But his mind was still clear.

'Maybe we could close the holes at the bottom of the lake with big rocks?' he suggested.

'That is a good idea, but I am not sure if it will work. Maybe we can use the magic potion to harden the rocks so they do not melt or break when they come into contact with the lava?

'But what if the volcano is not subdued by simply closing the holes? Perhaps something else is required to stop the volcano?' the Dragon questioned the Panther's suggestion. Her voice was full of doubt as her intuition told her that it would not be that easy.

'I honestly do not know what the right solution is,' she said. 'My mind is clouded. I need to listen to my inner voice. I need to focus my animal spirit on finding a solution.'

'We need to focus *our* spirits on finding a solution,' the Panther insisted. 'We are in this adventure together now!'

'Let us sit here at the foot of the volcano, meditate and connect with the Universal Divine Spirit to find the answer. At the top, directly at the Crater Lake, I cannot quieten my mind as the danger is too close to detach my thoughts from it,' she said.

The Black Panther knew that finding an answer to the problem would not be easy. Although he realised that emptying their minds and tapping into the source energy of their spirits was necessary, he had difficulty with the concept of meditation.

He liked to take action or think a matter through carefully instead of connecting with his spirit and aligning with the Universal Divine Spirit. He knew that something greater than themselves was out there, but he was not sure if that 'something' guided all living beings on this earth.

'Do you remember the meditation that we once did together?' the Dragon asked him.

The Black Panther remembered it well. It had happened on the night when he told the White Tigress his story. Before sunrise, they had gone outside the Panther's cave, and the Tigress had said that she would like to share something special with him.

The Panther had been curious, and the Tigress had taken him to a sandy patch on the shore of the Great Waterhole, where she had drawn a large infinity symbol in the sand.

'Please lie down in one circle,' she had instructed him as she lay down in the other circle of the symbol.

'Close your eyes,' she had guided him. 'Now place your paw in the middle, where the two circles meet.'

When he had done so, she had put her paw on his paw. They had lain for a while in their separate circles. Neither the Panther nor the Tigress had said anything, but both had felt the energy flowing between them.

It had been as if the energy was coming from the night sky to the point where the paws of the two animals were touching, and it had felt as if the source energy of their two spirits was being exchanged between them, flowing back and forth.

Maybe it had just been a feeling that the two animals shared because they were in love, but maybe it had been something inexplicable that had happened outside the physical realm.

Although the Panther had never meditated before, he had felt clear in his mind and light in his heart afterwards. The two animals could not explain what had happened that night, but since then, they had felt even more connected through their spirits.

In the same way as she had done before, the White Dragon drew a large infinity symbol in the soil so that she fitted in one circle and the Panther in the other. Both animals lay down, and this time, the Panther's paw rested on her claw.

It was a peculiar scene, with the two animals lying calmly at the foot of the volcano while the lava erupted from the Crater Lake at the top of the volcano, not far from them.

Both animals felt that their only chance to find a solution to stop the lava was to calm their minds and to listen within. They concentrated, emptied their minds and went into a meditative state.

Their animal spirits tapped into the Universal Divine Spirit, and they connected with the Golden Hare.

To tame the volcano, you will need to close the holes at the bottom of the Crater Lake with big rocks. There are three holes, and you will need to work together; you cannot succeed alone.

This will, however, not be sufficient to quieten the volcano. Each of you will need to perform a selfless act of unconditional love towards the other. Only then will the Tiny Island be saved. You need to hurry; there is not much time, the Hare explained telepathically.

Both animals immediately broke from their meditative trance after the instruction.

'Jump!' the White Dragon said, and the Panther jumped onto her back. She flew with the Panther on her back to the top of the volcano and stopped at the shore of the Crater Lake.

'Do you know what the Golden Hare meant by an act of unconditional love?' the Panther asked.

'I honestly do not. Maybe he means that we have to protect each other when we try to close the holes,' she answered.

'At least we have clarity now that we have to close the three holes at the bottom of the lake. We will throw the big rocks into the lake, which will hopefully plug the holes in the lake bed. We have to throw them in precisely, as I do not know whether we will be able to dive down,' the Panther explained to the Dragon.

'That seems like a good idea. It would be unwise to dive down into the Crater Lake. The Red Firedragon died in the lake. What if his animal spirit has been transformed again and he is still alive?' the White Dragon voiced her concerns about the evil spirit.

The Black Panther did not have an answer.

'We cannot risk that. You are right. His spirit might have transformed into something else. We should not dive into the lake but instead throw the rocks from above. I will sit on your back and direct you where to toss them. You will have to carry them in your claws,' he suggested.

'How do we make sure that we precisely hit the holes at the bottom of the Crater Lake?' she asked him, her voice again full of doubt.

For her, the whole endeavour was an almost impossible task. How could they ever stop the eruption?

The White Dragon was lost in her thoughts. She looked at the three lava fountains shooting into the sky. As she had once seen a volcano erupt in the Asantian rainforest and the destruction it had caused, she felt that it would be an impossible task to stop an active volcano.

But then she remembered that the Golden Hare had never misguided her. He always seemed to know what had to be done. They had to trust that the Universal Divine Spirit was guiding the Hare and would also protect their endeavour.

'I still have no clear idea how we should approach this challenge. I hoped when the Red Firedragon died that I had fulfilled my destiny. And now we have another task in front of us,' she addressed the Panther and sighed.

'Do not give up! White Dragons never give up.

You will see—we will find a solution because we are together. Together, we can fight anything,' he replied.

'You are right!' she said, re-energised by his optimism. The Tigress had never given up, and the White Dragon would not give up. Together, they would be stronger and find a solution. They were both fighters.

'How do you eat an elephant?' the Panther joked and smiled.

'One bite at a time,' she answered instantly as she knew that this was his favourite analogy for how to solve tasks that seemed impossible at first.

The Dragon picked up a large rock from the ground, and the Panther jumped onto her back. He would be her navigator.

Before she began to fly towards the three lava fountains, she put three drops of the magic potion onto the rock as instructed by the Wise Cat. She hoped that the potion would help them to perform a seemingly impossible task.

'Now you have to fly slower,' the Panther suggested after they took off with the rock in the Dragon's claws. 'When I say "now", you drop the rock, and hopefully it will close one of the holes and extinguish the first fountain. You need to fly higher now. We must drop the rock from high above so that it directly hits the lava fountain and plugs the hole.'

The White Dragon could not see where she had to drop the rock so it would find its way into the hole. But she followed his instructions as she fully trusted him. She reached out to his animal spirit so that they could synchronise their spirits.

'Now,' the Panther roared, and she dropped the rock. It fell directly onto the first fountain and pierced its way through the lava. Because it had been treated with the potion, it went straight through the lava and was neither melted nor broken apart.

The White Dragon flew back to the shore of the Crater Lake. They saw that one lava fountain had vanished. She looked content that they had been successful.

'You were right. There is always a solution. Thank you for having hope for both of us,' she said and smiled.

'There are still two holes to close, and one of the remaining lava fountains is much bigger than the other. Only when we have closed all three will we have completed the task and saved the Tiny Island,' he noted.

'I know,' the Dragon sighed. The Tigress had always been impatient in her life. Although she was much calmer now as the White Dragon, a sense of impatience was still deeply rooted in her. Even the meditation with the Golden Hare had not entirely rid her of this character trait.

She put three drops of the magic potion on a second rock and picked it up. They flew to the middle of the Crater Lake and dropped the rock onto the smaller of the two remaining lava fountains.

When they reached the shore of the lake again, they saw that another fountain had also stopped spraying lava into the sky. She was relieved that they had already managed to close two holes out of three.

'The biggest challenge still lies ahead. The third hole is much bigger than the other two. We need a big rock to close that hole,' the Panther reminded her. 'We will not find such a rock here. We need to fly down to the foot of the volcano to find one that is big enough.'

'Jump!' the Dragon said to the Panther, who sprang onto her back as she took off.

The White Dragon was slightly irritated because he kept telling her what to do. Even though she admired him for his skills in solving every problem, she was now secretly annoyed that he always seemed to give her orders. As she flew down towards the foot of the volcano, she thought about her attitude towards him and immediately decided that she had to drop her ego and let the Panther guide her.

She acknowledged that her ego pushed her to be fiercely independent, but she knew that male apex predators had a natural instinct to dominate their female counterparts. It was in their nature, and she could not change this. She just had to accept it, let it go and continue to stay in her power.

After searching for a while, they found a large rock at the foot of the volcano, and she put the last three drops of the magic potion onto it. The rock was massive, and it would be difficult for her to carry it up to the top of the volcano. Still, they needed a larger rock to close the last hole, as the final lava fountain was wider than the other two had been.

While the Dragon flew with the Panther on her back towards the Crater Lake, she realised why the Golden Hare had insisted that she do various strengthening exercises. She had learned how to control her mind and lift a weight that was heavier than her.

The Panther proposed stopping once they reached the top of the volcano, but she refused. She maintained that she could not halt at the lake shore.

'We just cannot waste any more time, and I would lose my flying balance if I made a stop,' she protested.

The Panther knew that he had no chance of arguing with her about this. She was as stubborn as the White Dragon as she had been as the White Tigress.

So he gave in, knowing there was no way to convince her. He felt she was struggling to carry the massive rock, so he connected to her animal spirit and supported her with his source energy.

The Dragon had to fly high above the Crater Lake to drop the rock onto the last lava fountain.

'Drop!' the Black Panther shouted, and she dropped the rock. It pierced through the lava, passed the surface of the water and seemed to sink towards the last hole at the bottom of the Crater Lake.

The White Dragon flew with the Panther towards the lake shore and looked at the lava fountain.

'It should disappear at any moment,' she said after a while. She was hopeful that they had concluded their task and closed the third hole, but the lava fountain did not disappear. It continued to shoot into the sky.

CHAPTER TWENTY-NINE

In the Abyss

'We may have missed the hole. We need to adjust the position of the rock,' the Panther suggested. The Dragon sensed that he was worried.

'Or maybe the hole is too big—' she sighed, shaking her head in disbelief. 'But then we have to find another solution.'

'We have no choice but to dive down and see where the problem lies,' he replied.

'I am afraid you are right that we have to dive to the lake bed and see if we can move the rock into the last hole. We cannot drop another rock as we have already used the last three drops of the Wise Cat's potion. There is no way that a rock, however large, could pierce the lava fountain unless it was treated with the magic potion first. It would either melt or burst into a thousand pieces before it reached the bottom,' the Dragon concluded.

'Do you think that the third rock lying on the lake bed still has its magic?' the Panther asked.

'There is no reason it should not,' she replied.

'Then it's decided: we have to dive to the bottom of the lake. But the Crater Lake must be deep, and there is no way that we can hold our breath long enough to dive down and come up again alive,' he voiced his concern.

'The Wise Cat gave me some magic balls and stones. I have used them for underwater walks in the ocean before. They work well. We have grey stones that will take us down to the bottom at a slow and steady pace. We also have blue balls with a trunk attached so we can breathe. Then we have green balls to bring us up again once we have pushed the rock into the last hole.

'The Wise Cat provided me with two of each, so we can dive together. She told me as I left your cave that I would have to dive into the lake to complete my task and that I would need help for this. I had sincerely hoped that she would be wrong this time, but she seems to foresee simply everything,' the White Dragon finished her explanation.

The Panther had listened carefully. He did not at all like the idea of diving into the Crater Lake, but there was no other solution.

'We will use the magic balls and the grey stones to reach the lake bed, where we will move the third rock into the hole,' he agreed.

They each wrapped two vines around their waist and attached one grey stone to the first vine and the blue and the green balls to the second.

'I will hold you in my claws as we sink down together. The most important thing is that you continue to breathe in and out evenly. It is a little like meditating. You quieten your mind, and you breathe slowly in and out,' she told him.

Although he was an apex predator, the Panther had never taken underwater walks as she had done. Most land animals were afraid of diving into the ocean, the Dragon reminded herself. Only rarely did those animals develop a passion for underwater walks, even if the equipment that was made by the Wise Cat for the purpose had never failed so far.

'Ready?' she asked the Panther, who nodded. She flew with him in her claws towards the middle of the Crater Lake, far enough—but not too far—from the last lava fountain. The Dragon dropped into the lake, looking deep into his blue eyes before the water engulfed them.

The two stones unfolded their magic and took them down at a slow and steady pace. The Dragon held the Panther tight while they breathed in and out slowly through their air trunks.

Whereas the underwater world of an ocean is colourful and diverse, this was not the case in the Crater Lake. As they sank deeper, it simply became darker. The only thing they could see was the red lava fountain shooting up from the bottom. It would take some time before they reached the lake bed.

The White Dragon knew from conversations that she had had with the Brown Bear that the Crater Lake was fairly deep. Although the Bear had significant experience of taking underwater walks in the ocean and loved the challenge, he had told her that he had never tried diving in the Crater Lake, even though he thought that it was doable.

The Dragon felt uncomfortable because she did not know precisely how deep they would have to dive before reaching the bottom. Even if the task was not impossible, it would be risky.

The darkness that surrounded them added to her discomfort. She did not know why, but her intuition told her that deep in the lake, something evil awaited them.

It almost felt as if the Red Firedragon had tainted the Crater Lake with his evil spirit when he died. As they dived slowly, she had the same feeling of disgust that she had had when her spirit touched his spirit for the first time.

She felt a deep unease, but she calmed herself as she sought alignment with her source energy and reached out to the Panther to share her regained peace. As they could not talk underwater, the only way for them to connect was through telepathic communication or the alignment of their spirits.

She was not at all surprised when she felt that the Panther was fearful.

I feel that you are anxious. All is fine. You need to calm down. We are simply underwater. I think that we will reach the bottom of the lake soon, she said telepathically, trying to calm him.

I am not worried about being underwater. I am afraid because I feel deep in my animal spirit that the evil is in the lake and surrounds us right now. Not even your pure spirit can soothe me.

I feel the touch of the ultimate evil just as I felt it when we were fighting against the cruel Lion Brothers. I saw their cruelty towards other animals before we could stop them, and it wounded my spirit deeply, he replied mentally.

The White Dragon was used to the fact that they mirrored each other in their thoughts and intuition, but the intensity of his fear surprised her. Although she also felt uneasy, her white spirit prevented her from being sucked into the dark energy of the evil.

She had become much better able to manage emotions of fear, despair and sadness since practising meditation with the Hare and could more easily connect to her own source energy.

With the Black Panther, it was slightly different. Even though he had always fought for a good cause, he had killed many animals in the course of this fight, and he had seen too many cruel things in Avaria.

He had told her once that he felt tainted by the evil that had surrounded him. Deep inside, he had regrets about killing other animals.

When she was still the White Tigress, she had told him that he should forgive himself for his shortcomings and forgive others for theirs, but that was something that the Panther had not yet learned to do.

It was as if the fear had become part of his animal spirit—the deep fear that the evil would ultimately get hold of him.

We will be careful. Do not focus on your fears! Do not look into the abyss but focus on the light that shines inside you.

I feel that the source of my light is actually in my heart. It feels very different from my heart as the Tigress—more like a heart made of light than a heart made of flesh.

The evil will not get us even if the spirit of the Red Firedragon is still down here in the lake, she encouraged the Panther.

Thank you. Together we can fight anything, he replied to reassure himself. He was relieved that she had understood his deepest fear. It was not the fear of fighting against the evil but the fear of becoming evil himself while fighting against it.

When they reached the bottom of the lake, they had to find the third rock. It must be lying somewhere close to the lava fountain, the Dragon thought.

She again reached out to the Panther, but his mind was closed off to hers entirely. She still felt his animal spirit, but she could no longer communicate telepathically with him.

So they walked together towards the lava fountain in silence. Magically, the grey stones that the Wise Cat had given her had helped them sink to the bottom of the lake but did not weigh them down so much that they were unable to walk on the lake bed.

Although there was almost no visibility, the Wise Cat's magic potion helped them find the rock, which was shining with a white fluorescent light. It lay not far from the lava fountain.

The White Dragon was relieved that they had found it. They just had to roll the rock across the muddy lake bed and push it into the hole to plug the lava fountain.

Since the Wise Cat's potion had already been applied to the rock, the White Dragon was confident that they would be able to complete the task. Then they could float to the surface.

When they reached the rock, they started to push it towards the large hole where the lava was coming out. The Dragon's mind was fully focused on the task; she had detached from fear.

She again reached out to the Panther's spirit to align her own with his, but she was repelled. Through their spiritual connection, she could feel only that his spirit was still full of fear—fear of meeting the evil and aligning with it.

She tried to connect telepathically, but his mind was still closed off. Neither at the spirit level nor at the mind level would he let her in.

They worked together in silence, but the Dragon's thoughts were spinning. She wanted to tell him so many things, but she could not. She wanted to say to him that fear attracts the evil, that the evil feeds on fear. She also wanted to tell him how much she loved him, and that as long as they were united in this love, nothing could defeat them.

They fixed the third rock in the hole, and the lava stopped. They had succeeded, and the Tiny Island would be saved from the destruction caused by the volcanic eruption.

The White Dragon felt deep relief that they had completed their task. In the midst of adversity, she embraced the Panther and gave him a hug. She sensed the tension and fear that had built up inside him slowly subside, and his mind opened up again.

We have only to drop the grey stones that are attached to our vine belts, then touch the green balls, and we will float up, she explained to him telepathically.

The moment she dropped her belt with the grey stone that was keeping her down, a Giant Watersnake came out of nowhere, pushed the Panther aside like a little furball and wrapped himself swiftly around the White Dragon.

The Watersnake squeezed her body so that the Dragon could neither take in air nor breathe fire or spit frost. Her whole body—her wings, legs and claws—was immobilised, and her chest and lungs were compressed.

The Watersnake was so enormous that he would surely kill the White Dragon. Her skin started to glow, but that glow could not protect her from being crushed.

In the light of her glow, she saw that the Firedragon's spirit had transformed: the Giant Watersnake was red. With all her willpower, the Dragon tried to stay conscious, but she could hardly breathe in the stranglehold of the Watersnake.

Meanwhile, the Panther got back on his paws and saw that the Dragon was being crushed by the Giant Watersnake. In the light of the Dragon's glow, he saw that the evil had returned.

All the fear that he had felt before was gone. He was only fiercely determined to rescue the one he loved.

The Black Panther drew near to the Watersnake to distract him, but he took no notice of the Panther. He was simply too enormous and would have been able to swallow the Panther in one bite.

The Giant Watersnake kept his eyes on the prize, which was the White Dragon. He had no interest in fighting the Panther; he was too powerful to be bothered with him.

The Panther instantly knew that he needed a plan. Although the Dragon still had her air trunk in her mouth, he could see that the air was not reaching her lungs as they were compressed too tightly in the embrace of the Watersnake.

He realised that he could not reach the green stone that was tied to the vine around her waist. Unless he could touch it, she would not be able to float up to the surface.

The Panther made a decision, and even though he did not like the solution, it had to be done. There was no other way. He kept the vine with the grey stone attached tightly around his waist and took the second vine, with the green and the blue balls, in his paws. The trunk attached to the blue ball was long enough to give him air.

Then he drew close to the Watersnake. The Panther could feel that the Dragon had in the meantime dived into unconsciousness. Yet their two animal spirits were intensely connected.

Say goodbye to your beautiful White Dragon. She will be gone soon, the Giant Watersnake addressed him telepathically.

The Panther could sense the Watersnake's schadenfreude because he would have to watch the one he loved die and there was nothing he could do about it. He felt that the Watersnake wanted to indulge in his torture and feed off his helplessness.

Everything went quickly now. When the Panther was close enough, he touched the green ball, and with the ball activated, he floated up slowly to the level of the Dragon's head. With one throw, he wrapped the vine with the green and blue balls around her horns. Then he held his breath.

The White Dragon started to float up slowly with the confused Watersnake still wrapped around her. In order to keep her at the bottom of the lake, the Watersnake wound the end of his tail around a large rock, but he had to loosen his grip on the Dragon's legs and waist.

Abruptly, he lunged towards the Black Panther. The Panther knew that he had only one chance. As fast as he could, he moved towards the back of the Dragon and activated the second green ball, which was attached to the vine around her waist.

As he did so, the Watersnake caught him and swallowed him in one bite. Then something happened that the Watersnake had not expected but that the Panther had calculated precisely: the grey stone wrapped around the Panther's waist pulled the Watersnake back down. The stone unfolded its full magic powers and held them both on the lake bed.

Meanwhile, the two green balls, one attached to the Dragon's horns and the other to her waist, unfolded their magic and catapulted her upwards.

The pull of the two green balls was strong, and the Dragon slid out of the Watersnake's grip, while the Panther's grey stone simultaneously pulled him down.

The Black Panther had achieved the impossible. He had freed the White Dragon and saved her from certain death, and he had made sure that the Watersnake was held at the bottom of the lake so that he could not swim after her. By sacrificing himself to save the White Dragon, he had performed an act of unconditional love towards her.

As the Dragon shot up from the deep waters, she regained consciousness. She was worried that she did not know where the Panther was. She hoped that he had been able to rescue himself, but she could not be sure of that.

She knew that only when she reached the water's surface would the green ball lose its power. Once she broke the surface, she spread her wings and flew towards the shore. She was still weak from the encounter with the Watersnake, but drawing on all her willpower, she managed to reach the shore.

When she sat down, she found the Panther's waistbelt wrapped around her horns. She instantly knew that he had sacrificed himself to bring her safely back to the surface.

She did not know exactly how the Panther had managed to free her, but he had found a solution at the cost of not being able to come out of the abyss himself.

Her heart filled with endless love towards him for this act of unconditional love. But she also felt a deep sorrow and grief for the life that had been lost.

It was as if a thousand swords were piercing her heart at that moment. Sometimes love is purest when it hurts most, she thought.

CHAPTER THIRTY

The Loss

The White Dragon sat on the shore of the Crater Lake and waited for a miracle to happen. She reached out to the Panther's spirit in the hope that he had managed to save himself and make it to the surface.

She could still touch his spirit, but it felt distant and very different—as if eternal darkness was wrapped around it. She cried for the first time in her dragon life. They had managed to close the third hole, yet she felt that everything was lost.

The Black Panther had sacrificed himself to save her and the Tiny Island. The evil was still in the Crater Lake, and the Panther could not have survived in the abyss for so long.

How long would the peace on the island last? Would the Giant Watersnake resurface and cause more harm? How could she find serenity if the one she loved was gone?

The White Dragon was deeply saddened. All that she had wished for was that the evil would be gone for ever and they could live in peace and harmony on the Tiny Island.

She knew that this was naïve, and that the evil could always resurface somewhere else unexpectedly, but this did not change the fact that she felt she had not fulfilled her destiny. Her mind reached out to the Golden Hare and connected to his.

Congratulations, you have managed to close the holes in the Crater Lake. You have saved the Tiny Island, she heard the Hare's voice in her head. He sounded almost ecstatic.

But the Dragon was dissatisfied.

We have only saved the Tiny Island for now. The evil is still in the abyss of the Crater Lake; it can come up at any time. And I have lost the one I loved. He sacrificed himself for me, she replied telepathically.

In a vision I saw the Black Panther jumping into the mouth of the Watersnake to free you. It was not only brave of him, but also showed his deep love for you. Not many animals would sacrifice themselves to save the one they love. He truly showed what his animal spirit was capable of.

We cannot let the actions of our past define us. Every new day, we should seek to bring light into the world by our efforts in the here and now. White Dragon, what have you learned? What questions have been answered that you were seeking answers for? the Hare asked her mentally.

The Dragon thought about this long and hard and then felt the answer deep in her spirit.

There is a balance—a balance between good and evil. This balance will be maintained until the Universal Divine Spirit decides otherwise.

We could not defeat the evil. If one evil were destroyed, another would be created to keep the balance. All we can do is find alignment with our source energy, and then our destiny will align with us as well, she answered.

The White Dragon sounded wise, but then her despair over the loss of the Panther manifested. *His sacrifice was in vain as we did not defeat the evil,* she said and sounded almost angry.

I think you are being way too harsh on him. He performed an act of selfless love for you and the Tiny Island by rescuing you and by trying to defeat the evil.

In expressing his love that way, he made the Tiny Island a better place where the darkness no longer rules by pushing the evil back into the abyss. His act of unconditional love also showed something to you that you were uncertain about before. Do you know what I mean? the Hare asked.

Yes, I felt intensely connected to his spirit when the Giant Watersnake had me in a stranglehold. It was as if his spirit supported me, trying to keep my body alive, and I felt whole within myself.

I experienced an intense spiritual bond between us. I was for the first time certain that he was my missing other half, my twin animal spirit. My spirit wanted to stay united with his. I experienced a connection with the Universal Divine Spirit at the same time, and I tapped not only into my source energy but also into the Panther's.

Deep in my spirit, I could sense his intense pain and all his fears and sorrows when he sacrificed himself. I still feel his animal spirit, even though he is dead now. How can we still be connected? the White Dragon asked the Hare.

I cannot help you any further right now. You have to find out for yourself. Please meditate now to quieten your mind. It will do you good as you will need all your strength.

And remember that we should always stay in the love that we feel inside us and that we should be true to this love. I will come to the Crater Lake later and meditate with you, the Golden Hare promised.

The White Dragon started to meditate on the shore of the Crater Lake. At first, tears were running down her cheeks, and her thoughts were spinning. Only after a while could she concentrate again on the mantra 'Om'.

The feeling of despair and sadness slowly went away as her thoughts focused on the mantra. But then they wandered back to the Panther.

Why had she not been able to save him? Why could she still feel his animal spirit? She had to quieten her mind again. Otherwise, she would not understand the path that lay ahead of her.

CHAPTER THIRTY-ONE

The Hat Rock

After the dust had settled on the battlefield, the White Cheetah instructed the Red Fody to fly to the West corner of the Tiny Island. She was to warn the animals there that the volcano was erupting and tell them to go to the North Shore, where they would have to find a way to get over to the Hat Rock.

The Giant Eagle was to inform the animals in the centre and the South. The Grey Wolf was to run to the East to urge all animals there to go to the North Shore, where safety awaited them. The three silverback gorillas were to lead what remained of the former Firedragon's army to the North.

After instructing the friends, the Cheetah ran back to her cave to collect Leo and Cham.

The Wise Cat landed the balloon on the battlefield. She instructed the Big Panda and the Brown Bear to find the lion family at the shore of the Great Waterhole and carry the wounded Lion to the balloon.

The White Lion was conscious again, but he would not be able to run the long distance to the North Shore, so he would have to be taken there, and the Young Lioness could not carry all three cubs.

After a while, the Big Panda returned, carrying the

Lion on his shoulders, and the Brown Bear brought two cubs. At his side was the Lioness, with one cub in her mouth.

The Big Panda laid the Lion carefully into the banyan tree basket that was attached to the balloon. The Brown Bear, the Young Lioness and the Wise Cat climbed into the basket as well, and the Bear steered the balloon towards the North Shore.

Young Cham and Young Leo were happy when the Cheetah arrived at her cave.

'Where is my mama?' Leo asked, and the Cheetah explained briefly that his mother had transformed into the White Dragon and that she had successfully defeated the Red Firedragon, who was the former Capricorn.

She also told the two young predators that the Firedragon had caused the volcano to erupt and that they would have to move quickly to the North Shore and reach the Hat Rock, where they would find safety.

The whole story of the transformations was not easy for Young Leo to understand. It made him sad that his mother was no longer the Tigress but the White Dragon. Even though he was almost grown up, he sometimes still cuddled with her.

The White Cheetah laughed her unique cheetah laugh, but she understood that Leo, although as fiercely independent as his mother, sometimes still needed to be close to her.

'She will always be there for you and love you. And one day, you will decide that you are big enough to go your own path, and then your ways will part,' she replied.

'I am already old enough to take my own path. And I will prove it to everyone! The North is green, and we should find vines in the woods that Cham and I can use to tie planks and tree trunks together into rafts to take all the animals to the Hat Rock,' Young Leo maintained.

The Cheetah knew that he loved inventing interesting things with Cham. And he enjoyed to talk to other animals about his many plans for how to make the Tiny Island a better place. He had even spent some time with the Brown Bear, who had told him what exciting inventions he had planned.

He admired the Bear for being both strong and creative. When Young Leo heard from the Cheetah that the Brown Bear had invented a balloon, his fantasy took flight.

'We can use this balloon to carry the animals to the Hat Rock. We have to find a way to move the balloon back and forth from the North Shore to the Hat Rock. Together with the Bear and Cham, I will invent a device to do this!' he proclaimed.

As the White Cheetah lived in the North of the Tiny Island, they would reach the North Shore quickly. When the Cheetah left her cave, she was sad, but she could not show this to Leo and Cham. Not only had she lost the Black Jaguar, but very likely she would never see her cave again, unless the Dragon and the Panther could stop the eruption.

She had lived her whole life on the island and had enjoyed her life with Cham. She had appreciated her underwater walks with the Bear and the Tigress and had even loved arguing with the Red Fody from time to time.

And then things had changed so drastically. The Black Plague had emerged and threatened their existence.

The predators from Avaria had arrived and turned her quiet life upside down. She had fallen in love with the Black Jaguar and then lost him as quickly as she had found him.

She had had to fight in a battle although she had never fought before. Her friend the Tigress had transformed into a White Dragon, who was an unfamiliar animal to the Cheetah. And now the extinct volcano had erupted and was threatening the whole existence of the Tiny Island.

Sometimes she had not understood when the Tigress had sighed and told her that she felt burdened. Although the Cheetah shared the feeling at that moment, she knew that she would never give up and would rise again. She felt battered but not defeated.

The two young predators had already made their way to the North Shore, and the Cheetah had to run fast to catch up with them. When she got there, many animals had already arrived.

Cham and Leo were busy binding planks and tree trunks together with vines to build rafts to cross over to the Hat Rock. The ocean was calm, so the passage was possible.

Then the Bear's balloon landed. When the lion family, the Wise Cat and the others got out of the basket, Cham and Leo had many questions for the Brown Bear.

At the same time, the Wise Cat explained to the animals surrounding her that the White Dragon and the Black Panther were trying to stop the lava by diving into the Crater Lake.

But until they succeeded, the animals should prepare for the passage from the North Shore to the Hat Rock. Most animals did not entirely understand where the Wise Cat had this precise knowledge from, but they knew about her visions and trusted her.

The Brown Bear asked Young Cham to climb into the balloon, which he had tied with a vine to a big Flame Tree. Cham got the task of flying up in the balloon to keep lookout and shout when the lava fountains erupting from the Crater Lake stopped.

Meanwhile, Young Leo discussed with the Bear how to cross to the Hat Rock. They considered whether to use the balloon or the rafts that Leo and Cham had bound together.

Then something surprising happened.

'Look, there are only two lava fountains left,' Cham shouted.

The Brown Bear and Leo began to devise a plan for not only crossing over from the Tiny Island to the Hat Rock but also coming back again after the eruption had stopped.

While the other animals built rafts, the Bear and Leo would make a long rope by tying vines together. They would fix one end of this rope to a large rock lying on the North Shore. Then they would fly to the Hat Rock in the balloon and fix the other end of the rope there. Young Leo was excited.

'I now see only one fountain of fire left. They must have managed to extinguish the second fountain as well,' the animals heard Cham roaring from above.

'Let us still build the rafts and knot the rope together. We do not know whether they can stop the third fountain as well,' commanded the Cheetah.

The animals continued building the rafts and knotting the rope. They all waited for Cham to shout that the third fountain had also vanished. For a long while, however, nothing happened.

'The last fountain is gone,' Young Cham finally roared.

All the animals heard the hoarse voice of Cham from above. They stopped their work, laughed and celebrated the White Dragon and the Black Panther, who had halted the eruption and saved the Tiny Island. They did not know what price the two animals had paid for saving them.

CHAPTER THIRTY-TWO

The Black Dragon

The White Dragon was sad because she felt that she had no hope of seeing the Black Panther again. She had been dwelling on this thought and started to meditate to push away the feeling of devastation.

Suddenly, something tingled inside her. Warning bells went off, and her intuition told her that it was not over yet. She heard a deep sucking sound from the Crater Lake. When she opened her eyes, she saw that the surface of the water was moving.

She flew towards the middle of the lake to get a better look from above. A vortex was sucking water down towards the bottom of the lake.

Then it reversed and spat out a giant Black Dragon. Two Giant Eels who had propelled him upwards vanished immediately into the abyss of the lake.

The White Dragon's heart leapt when she saw the Black Dragon emerge from the deep waters and fly low above the Crater Lake.

Her immediate thought was that it was the Panther's spirit, who must have freed himself from the Watersnake's stomach and then transformed into a dragon. She had instinctively known that he still had one transformation inside him.

But how was it possible? How could he have escaped

from the prison of the evil that had swallowed him alive? She had always admired him for the way he found solutions in seemingly impossible situations.

But a surprise awaited the White Dragon. The moment that she flew towards the Black Dragon to greet him, he breathed red fire towards her. Her skin started to glow and withstood the blast, but she tumbled backwards in the air.

In her joy at seeing the transformed Panther alive, the White Dragon had made a mistake. She had not reached out to the spirit of the animal in front of her before flying directly towards him. At once, she raised her defences.

A second blast of fire shot towards the White Dragon, but it failed to touch her because she had simultaneously breathed fire towards the Black Dragon to protect herself. Surprisingly, he stopped breathing fire at her.

The White Dragon reached out to the spirit of the creature before her, which was wide open and receptive. However, touching the Black Dragon's spirit was confusing. At first, she touched an evil spirit, and she felt the same disgust that she had felt when she touched the spirit of the Capricorn, the Red Firedragon and the Giant Watersnake. There was no mistaking it: the evil had returned.

But then she touched a lighter spirit. It felt far away. It was as if this second spirit was cocooned inside the evil spirit.

She sensed that it was the Panther's spirit. It was weak and faint, but if it was still present on the Tiny Island, then there was hope for both of them.

The White Dragon knew she would not give up on him in the same way he had not given up on her in the abyss.

'Finally, I have cornered you, and I will defeat you this time. The Panther jumped into my stomach full of bravery, but it did not help him. With his last thought as he was about to die, he wished for a transformation,' the Black Dragon addressed her.

'As he was still inside me, the Giant Eels could not transform his spirit without also letting my spirit enter this new body. My spirit is wrapped around his animal spirit, just as my Watersnake body was wrapped around the Panther's body.

'If you kill the Black Dragon, you will be killing not only me, but also the bodily vessel for his spirit. The sacrifice that he made was in vain. I will succeed, and even if you stop me, you will have to kill the body of the one you love,' the Black Dragon roared and laughed a dire laugh.

The White Dragon was shocked. Two animal spirits were inside the creature. If she defeated the Black Dragon, she would destroy not only the bodily vessel of the evil spirit but also that of the Panther's spirit, she acknowledged.

How could she defeat the evil spirit without killing the body of the one she loved?

The Black Dragon would indeed fight her until his last breath. As the evil spirit was wrapped around the Panther's spirit and dominated the Black Dragon, she would have to defend herself.

If she lost, the Tiny Island would be doomed. The reign of the Black Dragon, who had the strength of both the Giant Watersnake and the Panther, would be devastating. If she did not stand her ground and kill him, the island would suffer under his rule of terror and many more animals would die.

The Black Dragon breathed another blast of fire towards her. But the light inside the White Dragon was strong, and her glow protected her. She knew, however, that she would only be able to withstand him, not to defeat him.

Once more, the Universal Divine Spirit had maintained the equilibrium between good and evil. If she could not beat the Black Dragon in a fight, she would have to find another solution, she thought.

At that moment, she reminded herself of the Panther's act of unconditional love. The Golden Hare had said that they could save the Tiny Island only if each demonstrated a selfless act of love for the other.

Although the Panther had already performed his act of unconditional love, she had not. She intuitively knew what to do. She flew away from the Black Dragon towards the shore of the Crater Lake.

'You coward!' he roared after her and followed her towards the shore.

Calmly, the White Dragon sat down, started to meditate and reached out to the Golden Hare telepathically.

You are fighting the Black Dragon, and the Panther's animal spirit is trapped inside him. Do you remember the two circles and the signpost at the Energy Point of the South?

That is how you can strengthen the imprisoned spirit of the Panther. His animal spirit will grow only if the light grows within it. Remember that your spirits have to release their shadows before they can embrace the light within them.

I believe that fighting is not the solution. Only releasing your shadows and growing the light within you will allow you to perform an act of unconditional love towards his animal spirit.

That is the only way to defeat the Black Dragon and to rescue the Panther's spirit. I will come to the volcano to support you, but it will take me some time to reach the Crater Lake, the Golden Hare guided her.

The White Dragon recalled the Hare's instructions when they had meditated at the Energy Point of the South together. She understood that he was referring to the meditation to release the shadows and embrace the light. She was confident that she would be able to perform this meditation, but first she had to connect to the Panther's spirit.

The Black Dragon again shot red fire towards her, but the White Dragon's glowing skin withstood his fire.

'You coward!' the Black Dragon roared, furious that she was able to protect herself with her glowing skin. He approached, intending to fight her with his claws and teeth.

The two dragons closed in combat, biting into each other's flesh. But something was different now. The Black Dragon could not pierce the White Dragon's skin—neither with his mouth nor with his claws. She had remained in the Crater Lake for so long that her skin was now protected. The bites and scratches of the Black Dragon could no longer harm her.

The White Dragon had, however, made a deep wound in the Black Dragon's flesh. He had transformed only recently, and his dragon skin was still vulnerable. The Black Dragon was shocked, for this meant she could defeat him in close combat. He retreated.

That was the opportunity for which the White Dragon had been waiting.

I need to connect to the Panther's spirit, she thought. I need to send him my light and my love. When our spirits are connected, we can together release the shadows and embrace the light. There is no other way. The Golden Hare is right, she acknowledged.

She could, however, only reach out to the Panther's spirit, not communicate telepathically with him, as the evil spirit was controlling the mind of the Black Dragon.

Her spirit lovingly touched the Panther's spirit until they connected. His animal spirit was faint; it was hidden deep inside the Black Dragon, almost pushed aside by the expansive evil spirit.

But it was there. She had connected to the Panther's spirit, and that was all that mattered. Even though his spirit had many shadows, there was also a bright light shining inside him. With her love, she had to help him release his shadows and then strengthen the light within his spirit.

Meanwhile, the Black Dragon had regained his confidence and attacked the White Dragon with his fire, but as before, her white skin glowed and protected her.

As she was now deeply connected to the Panther's

spirit, she focused on the seven mantras that she had read on the signpost of the Energy Point of the South.

I release my fears, she silently recited the first mantra.

The White Dragon felt her heart become fearless. She also felt the anxiety in the Panther's spirit begin to vanish.

When the next blast of fire hit her, she remembered the guilt that she often felt towards Young Leo.

I release my guilt, she expressed mentally and noticed that her feelings of guilt towards Leo started subsiding. At the same time, she sensed that the feelings of guilt for killing so many animals that were deeply entrenched in the Panther's spirit began to vanish.

With each new blast of fire that the Black Dragon breathed towards her, she released another shadow in her animal spirit, and the Panther's spirit mirrored hers and released one of his shadows at the same time. It was as if they were much more potent in relinquishing their shadows because they were spiritually connected.

They released their anger, sorrows, lies, illusions. The White Dragon let go of her anger towards evil animal spirits, her sorrows about the Mountain Lion, the lies she had told Leo as a cub about his father, and the illusion that she would be able to protect everyone she loved. The Panther's spirit mirrored hers in releasing his shadows.

Finally, the White Dragon released her attachments to Young Leo, her parents and her friends. Her heart was free. She had let go of the past, and those shadows could no longer influence her present or determine her future.

She sensed that the Panther's spirit had also let go of his attachments. Both of their animal spirits were free from burdens, and she could feel that his spirit had become much stronger.

The Black Dragon was puzzled. Why would the White Dragon not defend herself? What was her strategy? He doubted that she had given up, but perhaps she did not want to fight him because the Panther's spirit was trapped inside him. The evil spirit could not reach out to her animal spirit as it was closed off.

'What are you trying to achieve? Have you realised that you will wipe out the bodily vessel for the Panther's spirit as well if you defeat me? You coward! Fight!' the Black Dragon roared, trying to provoke her.

He was full of anger and hatred towards the White Dragon and aimed directly at her dragon heart with his next fire blast. Even though she felt his fiery breath directly above her heart, she withstood and focused on positive thoughts. Then she started to recite mentally the seven mantras of light.

I call forth within me trust. She felt that her own and the Panther's animal spirits trusted each other deeply. Both believed that they would find the path towards the light together and defeat the evil.

She continued. Whenever another blast of fire hit her, she recited a new positive force.

I call forth within me creativity, will, love, truth and light. The light in her heart grew stronger with every mantra. She felt that the Panther's spirit was also full of light. The light was growing inside his spirit, although at a slower pace. But she kept hoping for the best.

She instinctively knew that with the last mantra, the bright light of the Panther's spirit would pierce the Black Dragon's heart and defeat him.

She also knew that the next fire blast from the Black Dragon that hit her heart would kill her, as her own heart would be bursting, too.

But she had surrendered to the path that the Universal Divine Spirit had chosen for her. When the Black Dragon's fire hit her heart once more, she absorbed the fire.

'I call forth within me letting go!' she recited her last words aloud.

For the last time, her spirit embraced the Panther's spirit. Then a massive blast of white fire erupted inside her, piercing her heart. At the same time, a thousand rays of white fire flashed inside the Black Dragon, piercing his heart.

The flames united and wrapped around the two dragons' bodies like a dome of white fire. When the fire died away, only a large pile of ashes was left.

Both dragons were no more. The White Dragon had sacrificed herself, together with the one she loved, so that the animals of the Tiny Island could live in peace and harmony.

The memory of their adventures would, however, be kept alive for generations.

CHAPTER THIRTY-THREE

The Phoenix Rises

The Golden Hare arrived at the shore of the Crater Lake after the fight between the dragons. He saw the pile of ashes, which was still smoking. He sat down, prayed to the Universal Divine Spirit and cleansed his spirit through meditation.

When he had finished, he took an empty coconut shell and scooped up some of the ashes to take back to the Energy Point of the South. Then he turned one more time towards the pile. A crystal-clear tear rolled out of the Hare's eye directly onto the ash pile.

A ray of sunshine hit the tear that had fallen onto the smoking remains of the dragons. The ashes were illuminated with white light while the Hare chanted a strange humming sound.

A big cloud covered the sun, and it started to rain. The rain stopped, and the sun came out. A beautiful rainbow appeared, and the Golden Hare smiled.

Out of the ashes, a strange creature flew into the sky with a loud cry. The Phoenix had risen from the dragons' ashes. After shooting into the sky, the bird returned to sit beside the Hare. He was taller than an eagle, and his body was white. At his breast, he had a pattern that looked a little like two hearts intertwined.

The Phoenix had one ocean-blue wing that looked as if it was made of water. The other wing was the red of a blazing fire. The Phoenix had an elegant tail with seven feathers; three were blue, one white, and three red.

'I have never seen an animal like you in my whole life, and I have seen many. But I have read about you in the ancient fables. You must be the legendary Phoenix. Welcome to the Tiny Island. I feel that there is only light in your animal spirit.

'From whose animal spirit have you been reborn? From the White Dragon's spirit? Or from the Black Panther's? Or from both?' the Golden Hare asked and smiled.

'I doubt that an evil spirit could rule such a magnificent creature as you,' he said. Then the Golden Hare stopped addressing the Phoenix, who had not answered so far, and reached out to the animal spirit of the creature in front of him, which welcomed the Hare's spirit in.

'The White Tigress asked the right questions when she meditated with me,' he concluded, while the Phoenix simply looked calmly and gratefully at the Golden Hare.

'I had the most peculiar dream last night. I came upon the ashes of two dragons. When I cried one tear onto the ashes, a Phoenix rose from them, just like you. The Phoenix flew up into the air and flapped his wings, and then something happened that I did not expect.

'In the air, the Phoenix divided into two birds at the place where the double heart-shaped print on the

Phoenix's breast had been. Then, a Blue Phoenix sat down on my left, and a Red Phoenix sat down on my right. I was speechless.

'After I had found my words again, I said, "This is not what was written in the scriptures. I did not expect two phoenixes to rise. I truly thought that you were the missing halves of each other's animal spirit and that you would reunite."

'Then the Blue Phoenix started to speak. "We are a twin spirit; we are each other's missing half. We can unite as one bird, and then our spirits merge and we are whole. We then have double the strength and endurance of one of us. But we also have different tasks to fulfil, and that is why we can be two. We have found our peace with each other because we can be one, but we do not have to be. It is our choice; it is our free will."

'Then I woke from this dream. Shortly afterwards, you contacted me telepathically, and I gave you instructions on how to defeat the Black Dragon. But I did not know what the outcome would be. The Universal Divine Spirit is mysterious in his ways. I knew only that I needed to hurry,' the Hare finished his explanation.

'That was a beautiful dream,' the Phoenix with the green eyes replied and suddenly looked sad.

'I wish your dream had come true. But sometimes, the Universal Divine Spirit has other plans for us. When we two dragons burned in the explosion of white fire, I wanted to unite with the Panther's spirit.

'I had no fears; I had no sorrows; I had no anger. I had fully released my shadows, and I had embraced the light. I believed during the meditation, when I connected to his spirit, that he had also released his fears and embraced the light.

'But his animal spirit pulled back. The shadows were still very much there. He had not fully released them. His spirit was in pain; he was confused. I could feel that his fears had returned to him because he had lost his bodily vessel with no hope that we could again transform.

'I wanted him to embrace our love and to have hope and faith that the Universal Divine Spirit would one day send us back.

'My spirit was full of happiness, as I felt that I would reunite soon with my missing half, with the one I loved.

'But his spirit was so confused and scared. He did not want to unite, and when your tear fell onto the ashes, I transformed into this mystic body of the Phoenix. I had to leave him behind,' she explained.

Now the Golden Hare also looked sad, as he understood that a spirit that should not have been lost was lost. But he also knew that the animals, and also their spirits, had free will in choosing their paths.

'What will happen to his animal spirit?' the Phoenix asked.

'The Panther's spirit was not ready to unite. You may have to travel together through many lifetimes before your spirits unite. But we can always expect miracles as long as we have faith, hope and love. Do not ever lose those three.

'It is said that love is the strongest of all forces and that it can overcome anything.

'Love itself has different vibrations but is connected

to the material world. All animals can experience physical love when they mate.

'Some animals are also connected at a mental level. That is a higher vibration, but between two lovers, the second level is not complete if the first level is not fulfilled as well.

'The highest vibration of love can be found at a spiritual level. That bond is rare, as most animals have not learned to embrace their own spirit. This is why they also cannot sufficiently connect with each other in the spiritual realm.

'If the love between two animals is true and pure, it will contain all three elements. That is why love is called the strongest force,' the Hare replied.

'Thank you for clarifying this for me. The Golden Watersnake explained this to me in different words when I met her at the Blue Bay. But I did not entirely understand it back then because I had not released my shadows and fully embraced the light.

'I felt that the Panther's spirit was my missing half, my twin spirit. But as he had not fully released his shadows, he could not embrace the light. He let his past determine his present, and so it could influence his future.

'I think that is why he could not unite with me. I understand now, and I cannot blame his animal spirit for not being ready,' the Phoenix said. 'How are hope and faith connected to our animal life and the physical, mental and spiritual realms?' the Phoenix wanted to know.

The Golden Hare thought long and then answered,

'I believe that hope relates to the mental realm, to our mind. Hope has no physical manifestation; it is a state of mind.

'Faith is related to the spiritual realm. If we do not have faith, we cannot connect to the Universal Divine Spirit, and we struggle to embrace our own animal spirit. But we need all three—faith, hope and love—to become whole.

'Even a twin spirit can thrive without its missing half. It is more challenging, but it is possible. The twin spirits want to be together, but they do not need to be together. They can also become whole in themselves. That is the lesson that you had to learn. You did well when you let go of the Panther's spirit.

'You did not follow him into the shadows; you chose the path of light. You understood that although your love for him was pure, only his spirit could save itself.

'For you, the task now is letting go. You can still live a fulfilled life in happiness and joy. I am glad that you had the spiritual strength to transform. A Phoenix does not often rise from the ashes,' the Golden Hare finished his explanation.

'I can let go of the Panther's spirit. I can lead a fulfilled and happy life as I have released my fears, guilt, anger, sorrows, lies, illusions and attachments.

'But I will always remember that nothing is impossible as long as I have faith, and I will also never lose hope. And as long as I call forth within me love, I will stay in alignment with the Universal Divine Spirit.

'I will not forget to remain in my heart space and not let my mind take over completely. If we love, there has to be a balance between our hearts and minds, but I strongly believe that our hearts should rule,' the Phoenix said.

The Golden Hare looked into her eyes and knew at that moment that she had not lost hope because the love and the light in her were strong. He decided to stay silent for now about the secrets that he had read in the ancient book of shadows. Instead, he focused on the book of light and continued with his instruction.

'The ancient scriptures say that the Phoenix can change into all animals from which she had risen. When you transformed into the White Tigress, your physical strength fully unfolded. You reached the full potential of your mental strength when you transformed into the White Dragon.

'As a Phoenix, you have now entered the spiritual realm of your existence. You should feel inside that you have all the strength, wisdom and power of the animal spirits of the White Tigress, the White Dragon and the Phoenix. In time, you will learn how to use them wisely.

'From now on, you should focus on developing your spiritual abilities and strive to become whole as an animal spirit. Only then you will experience being limitless.

'But you are not a golden animal yet. One day, you may become one. Until then, you will have to face more challenges and adventures,' the Hare explained and looked again into her eyes to search her inner being.

The Phoenix had a last question: 'What will happen to the evil spirit? I felt him briefly before I rose from the dragons' remains. That spirit was full of anger, sorrow and hate.'

'The evil will return one day to the Tiny Island. We have to be prepared. That is how the Universal Divine Spirit achieves balance in this world,' the Hare replied. He took a second coconut and filled this shell, too, with the ashes of the dragons.

'There are two animal spirits in the "In-Between" now. I do not think that they are entirely gone yet. I will keep the coconut shells containing the ashes safe at the Energy Point of the South and bury them in the holy soil. I hope that this will put the two spirits to rest so that they can be reborn one day and re-enter the circle of life,' he said.

Deep down in his heart, however, the Golden Hare knew that this was not the end. One day, not far in the future, the Phoenix would again embark on a dangerous journey. The Hare was sure of this, although he kept it to himself.

CHAPTER THIRTY-FOUR

Meditations

'You never concluded your exercises with me. We have never done the meditation for releasing the shadows and embracing the light together.

'I think I should teach you how to do that particular meditation. You tried the meditation, and even though you succeeded for yourself, you were not able to guide the Panther's spirit as there were just too many shadows inside him.

'We will do the practice here and now. You will not have time to follow me to the Energy Point of the South as you should make your way to the North Shore soon. But before that, I will show you this special meditation. It will conclude the lessons that we started when you came to the Energy Point,' the Golden Hare said and smiled.

He knew that it was still painful for her that she had not been able to save the Panther's spirit, but he had to refocus her mind on the present and the future. She could not be lost in the past.

'I am ready to follow your guidance,' the Phoenix replied.

'Then please sit down in a comfortable position. I will start with some breathing exercises before we meditate,' the Hare instructed her.

After they had completed their usual breathing exercises, the Hare explained to the Phoenix how he had discovered the meditation.

'This special meditation was developed aeons ago when the animals were still able to transform their spirits as part of their journey. But they have forgotten all about it. Nowadays, very few animals can successfully transform their spirit in the Underwater Waterfall or the Crater Lake. Most would perish if they tried.

'For a long time, I knew only the shadow-and-light meditation that was related to the signpost at the Energy Point of the South. All I knew was that you could go around the circles and release your shadows and embrace the light.

'Some time ago, however, I discovered in an ancient scripture how to do this meditation differently. You can do it anywhere, even if you cannot walk in the two circles. I will share it with you now.

'Each shadow and each positive force is attributed to one of the seven chakras of your body.

'Every animal has the potential of seven different animal spirits inside them, but most will encounter only the one spirit that they were born with.

With the meditation, you will be able to go mentally through the transformations that you have already experienced or will undergo in the future.

'And if you practise regularly, you will also learn how to physically transform your bodily vessel in alignment with your chosen spirit.

'But as we go through it for the first time, we will

focus only on the mantras and not on the actual physical transformations.

'The last chakra is attributed to the golden animals. You may get a glimpse of your future,' the Golden Hare explained and then sat down in a comfortable position.

The Phoenix was excited to practise her first meditation as the Phoenix—as an animal of the spiritual realm.

'Please close your eyes now and follow my instructions,' the Hare guided her.

'Connect to the body, connect to the breath.

'Inhale deeply, exhale slowly.

'The breath should be natural. Keep the same rhythm with the breath.

'Inhale deeply, exhale slowly.

'Imagine the place where you are. Wherever you are, relax and let go.

'Mentally visualise the body from the bottom to the top.

'Inhale deeply, exhale slowly.

'The whole body is now in a relaxed state.

'Prepare mentally to experience your transformations.

'Focus your awareness on the base of the spine, on the Root Chakra.

'Feel the Root Chakra, the Base Chakra.

'The Base Chakra is blocked when we have many fears. When we trust the universe, when we trust ourselves, we activate the Base Chakra.

'There are certain affirmations. I will recite them aloud and you will repeat them silently three times.

'I release all of my fears.

'Inhale deeply, exhale slowly.

'Repeat mentally another two times: I release my fears.

'Now you will repeat silently three times the following affirmation: I call forth within me trust.

'The colour of this energy centre is red.'

The Golden Hare paused so that the Phoenix could feel her animal spirit that was related to the first chakra.

The Phoenix saw the colour red and focused on it. She felt as if she was again the young Tigress living with the Mountain Lion and Cub Leo in the White Mountains.

She experienced intensely the fears she had felt when the Mountain Lion became more and more consumed by his greed. She relived the fear that she had encountered when he did not come back from the White Mountains and released those fears.

She had a vision of how she had left the White Mountains for the shore of the ocean. When she had pushed the plank into the sea, she had called forth within her trust. She decided that she would never forget that feeling of trusting her destiny.

'Now we move to the second energy point. It is a little above the Base Chakra.

'Feel the second energy centre.

'Feel the Sacral Chakra.

'Breathe in deeply, exhale slowly.

'Repeat mentally three times: I release all my feelings of guilt. And I call forth within me creativity.

'The colour of this energy centre is orange,' the Golden Hare instructed her.

The Phoenix saw the colour orange and felt as if she was Clumsy Tiger again. She remembered how she had arrived on the Tiny Island and how she and Strong Lion had fallen in love.

She felt the strong physical force between them, their emotional and spiritual connection.

Strong Lion had brought her back to life and reignited the raw nature of the Tigress. He had reawakened her animal spirit, which had been only faint after the loss of the Mountain Lion. She sensed a feeling of deep gratitude towards the Lion.

The Phoenix refocused her mind on the meditation.

'Now we move to the third energy point, which is on the Solar Plexus.

'Feel the third energy centre, which becomes stronger and active when you release all your feelings of anger and call forth within you will,' the Hare explained the third affirmation.

'Repeat mentally: I release my feelings of anger, and I call forth within me will.

'The colour of this energy point is yellow,' the Hare said.

The Phoenix repeated the affirmation mentally. She saw in her mind a bright yellow. She now remembered her time as the Fierce Tigress after Strong Lion had left her. Her anger had made her unjust and unforgiving.

But then she remembered how Cub Leo had softened her heart so that she had found the determination to again dive into the Underwater Waterfall and transform. She had activated all her willpower when she transformed into the White Tigress.

'Now we move to the fourth energy point, the heart.

'We find it behind the sternum.

'Focus on your Heart Chakra now.

'The affirmation is: I release all my sorrows. Repeat it three times.

'Then you embrace the positive force and repeat silently three times: I call forth within me love.

'The colour of the Heart Chakra is green or pink,' the Hare guided her.

The Phoenix saw the colour green. She vividly remembered her time as the White Tigress. She recalled how she had fallen in love with the Black Panther. She regretted that they had not spent enough time together, as most of their time had been dedicated to their duty to fight the evil. However, she felt gratitude for the love that they had given to each other.

'The fifth energy point is the throat.

'The affirmation is: I release all my lies, and I call forth within me truth. Repeat both three times.

'The colour of this energy centre is blue,' the Golden Hare continued with the meditation.

The Phoenix saw an intense blue colour. She could suddenly see through the lies that other animals had presented to her as she was no longer driven purely by her emotions but by her mind.

When she had become the White Dragon, it was as if the minds of other animals had opened up to her. She had been able not only to feel their fears, guilt, anger and sorrows, but also to see the lies that they told to themselves or others.

As the Dragon, she had ascended to be an animal guided by her mind. She had no longer hunted and had not wanted to fight other animals. Yet, as the White Dragon, she had had to endure the fiercest fights with the Red Firedragon and the Black Dragon. She understood that she had succeeded only because of her mental strength, her willpower and her connection to her true inner being.

'The sixth chakra is the Third Eye Chakra.

'Feel the Third Eye Chakra above the space between the eyes and repeat three times: I release all my illusions. And I call forth within me light.

'The colour of this energy centre is purple or deep indigo,' the Golden Hare instructed her.

The Phoenix saw the colour purple. She concentrated on the space above her eyes. She felt deeply in her spirit that she had entered the spiritual realm in her current transformation.

She understood that the Third Eye Chakra represented the ascension from the mental space to the spiritual sphere. She would now have to learn how to use her connection with the Universal Divine Spirit to bring light to the Tiny Island because she had released her illusions about good and evil.

She acknowledged that there would always be a balance. The Universal Divine Spirit maintained the eternal equilibrium between the light and the darkness in order for the animals to grow their spirits.

All animals had to decide every day which side they

stood on. Often, the evil would try to trick them and draw them to the shadow side with lies and illusions. The animals might believe what they were presented with because they wanted to trust. But deep down, their intuition screamed at them that it could not be.

Sometimes, animals wanted to believe illusions because they fitted their world. The evil created those illusions to distract them from the path of light and lead them into the shadows.

Only if those animals connected to their animal spirit would they understand their wrong perception. If animals developed this insight, they would be set free.

The Phoenix realised that faith in the Universal Divine Spirit could help the animals withstand the temptations and illusions that the evil portrayed to them. The evil might fool their hearts and even their minds, but it could never fool their spirits.

This was where the intuition of the Solar Plexus Chakra connected with the 'seeing beyond' of the Third Eye Chakra.

She acknowledged that illusions often served a purpose. In particular, animals wanted to believe those illusions if the evil masked itself as the good. Opening up their Third Eye Chakra would help animals to see through those wrong perceptions, she sensed.

The Phoenix breathed in and out, and the illusions that she had maintained were gone. She had also released the shadows of the past. She felt that she could now fully embrace her future.

'The last energy centre is at the top of the head. It is called the Crown Chakra.

'The seventh affirmation is: I release all my attachments. And I call forth within me letting go. Repeat three times,' the Hare recited the last affirmation.

'The colour of the energy centre is violet, white or golden,' he instructed her.

The Phoenix repeated the mantra silently three times.

She saw bright gold in front of her eyes. Then, a Golden Phoenix flew into the sky. She felt that this animal was whole. The Golden Phoenix had released all her attachments to the world and the animals in it. The Golden Phoenix was able to connect to the spirits of the other animals, predicting their destiny without interfering in it.

The Phoenix felt intense happiness when she saw this picture of her possible future in her mind. She then focused on her attachment to the Black Panther. Even though he was gone, she still felt the spiritual cord that connected the two of them. She understood that she had to cut this cord to embrace her future—to embrace love and light.

He had not succeeded in following her path into the light as there were too many shadows inside his spirit.

But she understood why she had met him. He was her twin spirit, and although she had always felt the light inside him, he had chosen a darker path throughout his lifetime than she had, and those shadows were haunting him when she wanted to unite with him.

She acknowledged that there was always balance within every spirit and that those twin animal spirits had both sides inside them, the light and the darkness.

If, however, the twin spirits met and could not fit together because one twin spirit had released their shadows whereas the other had not, the Universal Divine Spirit made sure that they could not unite.

If they united, the spirit would have to decide for one side: good or evil. But if those twin spirits were not in alignment or had not progressed in the same way, they would still be torn inside and fight their other half.

With him on her side, she had successfully faced her shadows, and the connection between them made her embrace the light even more strongly. She now felt deep gratitude towards the Black Panther and then released her attachment to him and let him go.

'Now all the energy points are recharged and activated. They are vibrating with positive energy.

'Feel balance, serenity, trust and love.

'Embrace the light and be in the present moment.

'Imagine the place where you are.

'Take a deep breath.

'Breathe in, breathe out,' the Hare continued the practice.

The Phoenix breathed slowly in and out. Her mind was empty even though she had tapped into the animal spirits of her transformations during the meditation. She felt re-energised.

'We conclude the practice by chanting three times the mantra "Om",' the Golden Hare said.

'Om, Om, Om,' the voices of the Golden Hare and the Phoenix sounded in unison across the shore of the Crater Lake.

'Take your time. Then slowly open your eyes,' the Hare finished with his instructions.

The Phoenix felt that she had again released her shadows and embraced the positive forces as she had done during her last meditation as the White Dragon. She had even seen a glimpse of the future. But one could never know for sure.

After saying thank you and goodbye to the Golden Hare, the Phoenix flew up into the air.

The Golden Hare gazed long after she had left for the North Shore. Then he made his way to the Energy Point of the South, in his paws the two coconut shells with the dragons' ashes.

CHAPTER THIRTY-FIVE

New Adventures

The proclamation ceremony for the White Lion as the new ruler of the Tiny Island was already in full progress when the Phoenix arrived.

Although the animals who had gathered at the North Shore wondered who this beautiful bird was, no one dared ask as she looked intimidating with her blue wing shimmering like water and her red wing shining like fire. The Phoenix sat quietly in a Flame Tree near the beach and listened to the speech of the White Lion.

'We have all fought bravely and defeated the evil that was brought to the Tiny Island by the Capricorn. We have reversed the spell that he cast over the island with his black magic, and peace was achieved when we won the battle.

'We will now all work together to eradicate the Black Plague around the Great Waterhole. I have already sent some of the remaining leopards to the Great Waterhole to collect the infected rodents, who will be kept safe until they either die or recover.

'Today, we pay tribute to our friends who fought against the evil and lost their lives. Today, we also remember the White Dragon and the Black Panther, who gave their lives to stop the lava eruption. We will always think of them and miss them.

'I declare myself the new ruler of the Tiny Island. I am the strongest predator on the island. The Young Lioness will be by my side, and the Wise Cat will be my adviser. My reign will be balanced, and justice will always be served,' the Lion roared.

He looked satisfied when he finished his speech, and all the animals roared, chirped, meowed and howled in agreement. They knew that although he was young, he would make a good leader. As he had chosen the Wise Cat to guide him, his reign would bring prosperity and peace to the Tiny Island.

The ceremony was interrupted by Young Leo.

'Where is my mama? I know that she is not dead. She cannot be dead. I love her so much. I feel that she is still alive,' Young Leo roared desperately as tears rolled down his cheeks.

All the animals looked with pity at Leo, who had lost not only his father but also his mother and the Black Panther, who had been his guardian.

At that moment, the Phoenix, who had so far just listened quietly, flew into the sky and landed on Leo's back. The animals surrounding him were surprised.

When he shouted, 'Mama, mama!' the animals watching him did not understand. Only the Wise Cat smiled.

'I am so glad that you are no longer the White Dragon. I would have been so afraid of you. I do not want you to be stronger than me! I want to be stronger than you—at least soon!' Young Leo roared, and his voice was full of joy.

The Phoenix rubbed her head against his. Then

she approached the White Lion and the Wise Cat and bowed her head in front of them.

'I am glad that you are the new ruler of the Tiny Island, and I am happy that you have chosen the Wise Cat to be your adviser. I will be the new guardian. For as long as it is necessary, I will stay here and protect the island,' she said.

'I am glad that you are back, Clumsy Tiger, and I am honoured that you will protect us,' the White Lion said and bowed his head to the Phoenix.

All the animals who had gathered at the North Shore started to laugh, and amidst the noise could be heard a loud cheetah laugh.

'Welcome back, Clumsy Tiger!' she roared and laughed again. Her laughter was the sound of relief.

The Phoenix flew back to the Flame Tree, where the Red Fody sat on the branch beside her.

Just as the animals were about to celebrate together at the North Shore, a school of dolphins arrived, with one of them carrying the Golden Watersnake on his back. Their leader addressed the land animals.

'Our ocean is in great danger. We have just come from the Blue Bay. The Blue Whale was stranded on the reef in the lagoon and died.

'Now a thick black liquid is running out of his mouth, which has already killed the fish around the Blue Bay. Please help us so that we can prevent the ocean from getting further poisoned. The situation is grave,' he maintained.

The land animals were shocked. They had just faced

the threat of the Black Plague and won a battle against the Red Firedragon, and the White Dragon and the Black Panther had stopped the erupting volcano. And now a new danger had appeared out of nowhere on the Tiny Island.

'What have we done to deserve this?' the Big Panda asked.

'Why is the Universal Divine Spirit sending us one threat after another? Will this ever stop?' the Grey Wolf added. Most of the land animals were annoyed.

The White Lion roared, and all the animals fell silent.

'Let the Golden Watersnake speak. I am sure that she can tell us exactly what happened. I have my own suspicions, but she knows best as she lives in the Blue Bay,' the Wise Cat addressed the animals at the North Shore, who now listened eagerly.

'The Capricorn passed by the Blue Bay when he was running away from Strong Lion. He had two large bags with him. I later learned from the dolphins that he gave those bags to the Black Dolphin, who hid the bags in the ocean,' the Watersnake explained.

'Later, the Blue Whale must have accidentally swallowed at least one of the bags. The Blue Whale became sick and died on the reef in the Blue Bay. We all felt sorry for him, but after a while, the thick black liquid began coming out of his mouth and started killing the fish in the lagoon.

'The sea turtles saved themselves by swimming into the open sea, but many other animals were caught off-guard. We need your help,' the Watersnake pleaded.

'In those bags were the magic potions and the poisons that the Capricorn took with him. Now I understand where he stashed them. I was concerned, but as his mind was completely closed off, I could not find out where he had hidden them. Everything going on with the Black Plague, the battle, the erupting volcano and the dying White Lion distracted me from the task of finding the potions,' the Wise Cat replied and sighed.

'It is not too late. We can still save the ocean surrounding the island, even if the Blue Bay is lost. But we have to act now. We cannot wait and waste precious time,' the White Cheetah roared. She started running directly towards the Blue Bay. The Phoenix rose from the Flame Tree and also made her way to the South.

'All other animals remain here for now. Together, we will come up with a plan for how to protect the ocean from further damage. I will coordinate who is helping where and who is doing what,' the White Lion roared.

'A true leader,' the Grey Wolf sighed.

And another adventure on the Tiny Island had begun.

The Unicorn and the Rainbow

After many decades, the legend of Clumsy Tiger was still alive. The young animals regularly came to the Flame Tree and listened eagerly to the stories that the ancient Red Fody told them about her.

Most of the old animals could not confirm the existence and transformations of the Tigress. The Tiny Island had been calm and peaceful for some time now. No battles were fought anymore, and none of them had ever encountered a dragon or the legendary Phoenix.

Many younger animals, therefore, averred that the Tigress had never existed. There was just no proof. Where were the Wise Cat, the Big Panda and the Grey Wolf? There was a large pride of lions on the island, but this did not prove anything. Thus, most animals said that the story of Clumsy Tiger should remain where it belonged: in the kingdom of fables.

But because the Red Fody was a wonderful storyteller, the young animals listened attentively to her. Sometimes, a courageous young animal asked questions: What happened to the White Cheetah? What happened to Young Leo? Does the Golden Hare still live on the Tiny Island? Where is the Phoenix now? What happened to the two coconut shells that were buried at the Energy Point of the South?

The Fody always answered patiently.

'I have not seen them for a long time. They all stayed on the Tiny Island initially. Their stories continued as they faced more challenges before peace and harmony were finally achieved. Some settled on the island, while others went into the world and made their own story.

'There are many more stories to tell. For example, how the brave animals saved the ocean around the Tiny Island from the poisonous potions of the Capricorn. Or the adventures of Young Leo, who grew up on the island and then discovered the world. Maybe Leo will return one day and will tell us his life story.

'I am just too old, and I cannot remember everything. I vividly recall only the story of the Tigress, as the events during that time changed life on the island significantly,' she chirped and sighed.

Most of the time, the young animals were content with this answer because there was hope that they would one day learn how the story advanced.

'We only ever hear the fable of Clumsy Tiger. Why can you not tell us one of the other stories? You are so boring!' the cheeky Young Elephant said one day.

The Red Fody looked gloomily at the Young Elephant. As she had a big heart, however, she said in a soft voice: 'The Tigress once told me the story of the Unicorn and the Rainbow. She was a fantastic storyteller herself, and I believe that she could cope with the hardships of her life only by telling Young Leo stories. One night, she revealed this extraordinary fairy tale to the White Cheetah and me.

'I think she was suffering greatly at that time because the Black Panther was paying no attention to her while he tried to prevent the Plague from spreading across the island.

'The Tigress understood this well, but because she had been abandoned by Strong Lion before, she felt neglected. I cannot blame her; the Panther rarely had time for her and Young Leo. He once told her that this world was not just rainbows and unicorns.

'"Even if the world consisted only of rainbows and unicorns," the Tigress replied, "someone would make sure that they, too, would face challenges. It is not about striving to live in a world of rainbows and unicorns; it is about overcoming those challenges and still feeling happy. The shadows of our lives rule us only if we let them rule. We can grow only if we release those shadows and embrace the light."'

The Red Fody finished her announcement of a new fairy tale and looked around. All the animals sitting under the Flame Tree were excited that the Fody had mentioned a new story. The Young Elephant could no longer hold back.

'Please tell us about the Unicorn and the Rainbow,' he burst out, after apologising for having offended the Fody, who gave a loud chirp full of joy and started the story:

Once upon a time, a beautiful Unicorn lived on a lush and green meadow in the middle of the jungle. She had a foal, who had been born some while earlier. The foal came from her union with the White Horse, whom she loved deeply.

One day, the White Horse ran off into the rain. The Unicorn was not that worried, as he always came back. This time, however, was different. He did not come back. The Unicorn searched for him for days, but she could not find him. Finally, she went back to her foal and carried on with her life.

One day, many full moons later, the Unicorn was running across a distant meadow early in the day to catch the morning sun. She liked it when the sun shone on her white hair and gave warmth to her body.

When it started raining, the Unicorn went to find shelter under the nearby trees, but as abruptly as the rain had started, it stopped. And then the Unicorn saw the most beautiful Rainbow she had ever seen.

The Rainbow was so close to her and shone so brightly it almost seemed as if he was looking at her. Usually, rainbows cannot look at animals, but this one was different.

Maybe the Unicorn could see the eyes of the Rainbow shimmering through the colours because she was a unicorn. Perhaps this Rainbow appeared that way because they were on a meadow where magic happened.

The Unicorn could not take her eyes off the Rainbow. She was fascinated by his colours, which she had never seen so intensely before.

But the Rainbow, too, could not take his eyes off the Unicorn as she was unique. He had only heard about unicorns before in the stories told by the animals who rested on his meadow. When the Unicorn had appeared on the meadow, the Rainbow had felt that the energy flowing across the meadow had changed.

He had already seen her galloping towards the meadow when he was invisible and was pleased that the rain had come after the sun so that she could see him in his true colours.

The Unicorn was a brave creature, so she decided to address the Rainbow.

'Hello, I am the Unicorn. I live on a meadow quite far from here,' she introduced herself.

The Rainbow was shy, but he managed to answer.

'I live here on this meadow. Sometimes, I also fly across other meadows, but I have never seen a unicorn before. I like the sheen of your white hair,' he added.

It was almost as if the Rainbow blushed for an instant, for at that moment, his colours appeared to be shining more brightly. After they had exchanged a few more words, the Unicorn said goodbye and vanished.

She had not told him which meadow she lived on. For some time, the Rainbow searched across the meadows for this magical creature, but he could not find her.

After two full moons had passed, the Rainbow saw the Unicorn again, standing near the lake on his home meadow. She was talking to the Fox. She could not see the Rainbow as it was bright sunlight.

Although he was able to appear if he drank from the lake, he was too shy to show himself while the Unicorn was speaking to the Fox. He did not want to disturb their conversation.

However, when the Unicorn left the meadow, she bowed her head slightly as if she wanted to say goodbye to the invisible Rainbow. He could not be sure of this, but he wanted to believe it and dreamt that night—and many nights thereafter—of the Unicorn.

The Rainbow could not forget the Unicorn. He had fallen instantly in love when he saw her the first time, and this attraction was only magnified when he saw her the second time.

Once again, he could not find her, even though he searched intensely. It was as if the Unicorn had the power to vanish into thin air, although she was not invisible in bright sunlight as he was.

One day, not long after he had sighted her the second time, he again saw the Unicorn on the meadow. Luckily, it had rained recently, so the Rainbow was shining in bright colours.

He did not dare talk to her, but the Unicorn addressed him: 'Good morning, Rainbow! We met some time ago. Perhaps you remember—I am the Unicorn. I was running across the meadows to find fresh grass today. I have travelled far this time as most fields are quite dry in summer. I just spoke to the Wise Owl, but I am now on my way home. Each animal can see me only three times; after that, they can no longer see me. That is my magic.

'But if I talk to them, they will be able to see me again. I do not know whether this also applies to rainbows—maybe, maybe not—but now that we have talked, perhaps you will always be able to see me. I am admiring your brilliant colours as I am completely white myself. Truly, I have never seen such brilliant colours before.'

The Rainbow smiled because he was happy that the Unicorn admired his colours.

'I am glad that the sun shone when you arrived and that it rained shortly afterwards because my colours are sparkling now. But even in broad daylight, the animals can see me if I want them to,' he replied.

'I can appear on this meadow as I can drink the water of the little lake here. Then I can show myself to whomever I want. I admire your white hair. It shines so brightly. I have never seen such a magnificent creature as you before. You seem so special. Would you like to spend a little time with me and talk?' the Rainbow asked the Unicorn.

Thereafter, the Unicorn came to the meadow every day, and they talked and talked. They fell in love

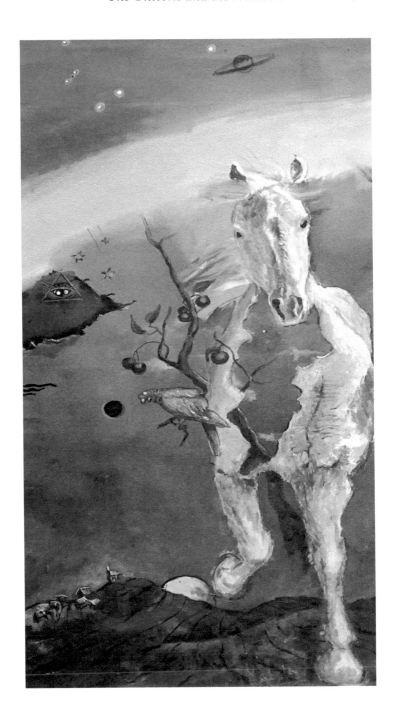

with each other, and soon the Unicorn and the Rainbow became inseparable.

The Unicorn was fascinated by the Rainbow's colours, which she had not seen so intensely before. She also enjoyed talking to him as he had seen a lot and was wise.

One day, the Rainbow confessed to the Unicorn:

'I truly love you, Unicorn. I have never felt this way before. You seem as if you are pure light. The energy level changed when you appeared on the meadow. When I met you the first time, I was so happy that I could appear in my most beautiful colours. Since meeting you, I radiate more brilliantly than ever.'

Indeed, the Unicorn could always see the Rainbow in bright colours after they met the third time as he made sure that he drank from the lake before she visited him. She could also see his eyes, which shone an intense blue.

However, the Rainbow hid his end. The Unicorn was curious and wanted to know why.

'Why can I see only your beginning and never your end?' she asked the Rainbow.

'We are at my home meadow. I do not show my end to anyone as I have been disappointed before. I do not show it even when I am in love.

'Nonetheless, I am astonished that I met you. You seem so different from the other animals. I have never seen a unicorn before. You must be one of a kind,' the Rainbow said, and his eyes were full of love.

'As far as I know, I am indeed the last unicorn in the jungle,' she replied, looking a little sad. 'There may be a few more scattered around the world, but I have never met another unicorn since my parents died. My foal is half unicorn and half horse, and he does not have a horn. I will tell you the story of the unicorns so that you will understand why we are so rare nowadays.'

The Unicorn began to tell him the story:

Once upon a time, there were many unicorns in the jungle. We preferred to live on the meadows inside the jungle as we loved the sun.

When other animals saw us, they spread the news about us. Although we were rarely spotted, many tales were told about us in the jungle.

We were wild and free. We were faster than horses, and we could jump higher than monkeys.

When the Monkey King heard this, he became jealous. He was the highest jumper among the monkeys and wanted to remain the highest jumper. He considered unicorns who could spring higher than he a threat to his reign.

Maybe the unicorns wanted to take his throne and become the new rulers of the monkeys, he thought.

The Monkey King had to prevent this coup. He asked his three advisers what to do. But none of them knew the answer. So he sent his messengers to the Hermit Monkey, who lived deep in the jungle.

All of them except one came back without an answer after two or three days and nights searching for the Hermit. They could not find him.

The last monkey was still missing and came back only many sunrises later. The other monkeys laughed at him. He came back dirty, with tree leaves in his fur and mud on his face.

'Why did it take you so long to find your way back?' a young monkey wanted to know.

'Maybe you found a female monkey and rested with her for a bit instead of searching for the Hermit?' another said and laughed.

'All of you be quiet. Bring him to the King,' one adviser said to the other monkeys. He was wise and old enough to tell from the shining eyes of the monkey who had come back so late that he must have some news.

So, the Messenger Monkey was brought to the King, who commanded that he be left alone with him.

The Monkey King wanted to know if he had found the Hermit and what he had said. He expected the Messenger Monkey to tell him how to catch a unicorn.

'You need to come with me and talk to the Hermit yourself. He is only willing to tell you in person. I know the way back to his tree. I marked it after I found him, so we will be able to meet him there. He is too old to come to you,' the Messenger Monkey replied.

The Monkey King did not like having to go to the Hermit, but he had no other choice if he wanted to capture a unicorn and understand their power to jump so high.

After a couple of days, the Monkey King and the Messenger Monkey reached the tree of the Hermit. It was situated in the middle of the thick jungle.

The Hermit Monkey was a wise old monkey who had served as adviser to the Monkey King's father.

'How do I catch a unicorn?' the Monkey King demanded to know from the Hermit Monkey.

'Why do you want to catch a unicorn? They are peaceful creatures and do no harm,' the Hermit answered.

'But they jump higher than I can, and I cannot accept other animals being able to spring higher than I. I am the Monkey King, and my subjects will disobey me and question my reign. They may even start following the unicorns instead of me,' the King screamed.

'I do not think that the unicorns would like to rule your monkey hordes. I also do not believe that the monkeys mind that the unicorns can jump higher than you. They all know that unicorns are magical creatures,' the Hermit replied as he wanted to calm the Monkey King.

'You should leave the unicorns in peace. They bring harmony and light to the jungle.

You should accept their presence and let it go. Imagine what would happen if they were no longer in the jungle. They bring happiness to the other animals and also to your monkeys.

'Do not resent them; simply accept that they can jump higher. I have to go now, Monkey King, as I need to tend to my fruit trees.

'Weigh my words in your heart and do not bring misfortune upon this forest. And please do not catch one of the unicorns. They may leave the jungle forever, and we do not want that to happen,' the Hermit Monkey explained.

After the Hermit said this, he escaped into the thick crown of his tree and vanished without saying a further goodbye.

The King was enraged by the behaviour of the Hermit, but he could not show this in front of his servant. Instead, he said harshly to the Messenger Monkey, 'None of this happened. I order you not to repeat a word that the Hermit just said—or else I will bite out your tongue.'

The servant knew that the King was cruel and that under no circumstances could he tell anyone what had happened.

So he bowed subserviently and said to the King, 'Certainly, Your Majesty, I will not tell anyone what the Hermit just said. I have actually already forgotten all about it.'

But the Monkey King could not forget what the Hermit had said. He was restless, for he

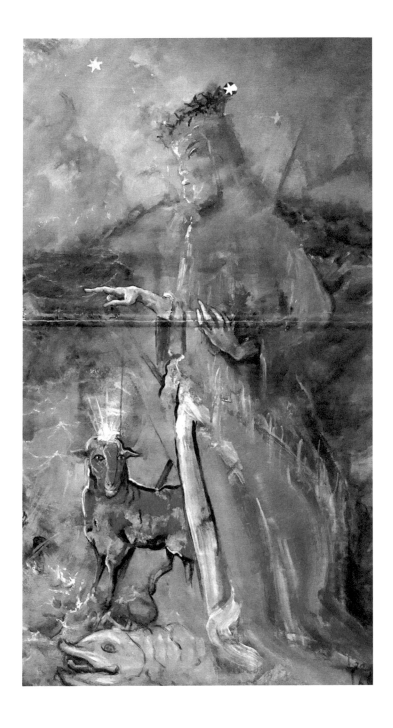

was still fearful that one day, one of his subjects would question his reign because he was not the highest jumper in the jungle.

Not long after they returned from the Hermit, the Monkey King called his advisers as he was still obsessing over the unicorns.

'I want to catch a unicorn. How can I catch a unicorn?' the Monkey King asked his advisers. All the advisers fell silent.

They were used to the wrath of the King whenever they did not immediately come up with an answer, but they still did not know. And better than the wrong advice was always to give no advice.

At last, the oldest adviser signalled that he wanted to say something to the King, who gave a sign to the adviser that he could speak.

'Your Majesty, I once heard from an old and wise monkey that you could catch a unicorn using a young female animal as bait. She would be able to tame the unicorn and touch it, and then we could throw woven vines over the unicorn to catch it. The vines would have to be strong, as unicorns are powerful', the adviser suggested.

The Monkey King liked the idea of catching a unicorn this way.

'We need a beautiful young White Horse to catch a unicorn. Maybe we can even put a twisted stick on the horse's head so that she looks like a female unicorn—just to be sure that my plan works,' he said, content that he had had such a brilliant idea.

All the advisers nodded and praised the wisdom of the King. They knew that he was vain and that they needed to express their admiration if they did not want to be punished.

The plan was put into action. They found a young female White Horse whom they forced to act as bait to catch a unicorn. They put a twisted stick on her head so that she almost appeared to be a unicorn.

The monkeys knew that unicorns loved to come to the meadows when it was a full moon as they enjoyed the bright moonlight. The next night was a full moon, and they placed the White Horse on the meadow.

They bound her with a strong vine to a tree in the middle of the meadow to make sure that she did not run away as she was anxious and did not want to be there.

In the crown of the tree, the King placed three monkeys with a large net made from strong vines with which they could catch a unicorn. They threatened the White Horse, telling her that they would kill her if she disclosed the plot.

Night came, and with the White Horse tied to the tree, the monkeys waited to see whether a unicorn would appear.

The Monkey King made sure that all the other monkeys were hidden in the crowns of the trees surrounding the meadow. They had strong sticks with which to beat the unicorn unconscious should he defend himself.

When it was completely dark, a unicorn approached the meadow. It was a young Male Unicorn. He was inexperienced and had no idea that other animals could harm him. He was also prideful and convinced of his strength.

When he saw the beautiful White Horse, he was immediately drawn to her. With the twisted piece of wood on her head, he mistook her for a unicorn. He came nearer as he was fascinated by this mysterious, beautiful creature whom he had never met before.

'Hello, I have never seen you before. You

must be from somewhere else as I know all the unicorns who live in the jungle.

'Are you lost? I think you may need my help. Maybe I can assist you in finding your way home. Or maybe you want to stay with me?' the Male Unicorn addressed the White Horse.

He was flirting with her and wanted to impress her. The White Horse did not know what to say. She was scared to death and did not dare speak as she feared the monkeys who were hiding in the trees nearby. Instead of speaking, she simply nodded.

'Oh, you seem to be very shy,' the Male Unicorn concluded and continued to pursue her.

As the White Horse was so scared, she lay down in the grass beside the big tree.

Fatefully, the Male Unicorn did not notice that she was bound to the tree. The fire of love was already burning in his heart.

Perhaps he did not notice that she was bound because it was night, and the moonlight did not give much away.

Maybe, he was simply so consumed by his quickly inflamed passion for her that he did not pay close attention. But this would seal his fate.

The Male Unicorn took her shyness as an invitation. He lay down next to her and started caressing her.

At precisely that moment, the Male Unicorn was caught in the trap. The monkeys in the tree above threw the net over the Male Unicorn and the White Horse. Quickly, they jumped down, and all the other monkeys came to hold the ropes of the net.

But the Male Unicorn was too strong and kicked wildly with his hooves. He was scared because the net had come down so fast and he did not know what had happened.

The Monkey King was screaming that the monkeys should hold the vines tight; otherwise, he would kill them himself.

The monkeys used their sticks to beat the Male Unicorn, because they were scared, too.

But the Male Unicorn did not calm down. He became wilder and kicked more aggressively.

So the monkeys also became more hostile and hit him harder with their sticks until he was no longer moving.

It was as if the fear of the monkeys had driven them to rage. When they lifted the net, there was blood everywhere.

The Male Unicorn was dead. Now the monkeys realised what they had done, but it was too late. They had killed the innocent Male Unicorn just because he was defending himself against being caught. And they had also killed the young White Horse.

The monkeys were shocked by their own rage, and not long afterwards, the council of elders decided to banish the Monkey King. He had to leave the jungle and was never seen again.

Also, the unicorns were never spotted again from that day forwards. After the monkeys slaughtered one of their number, the unicorns decided to move away from the jungle.

They scattered around the world as they could not agree among themselves where they wanted to settle down.

I was a new-born foal then, so my parents decided to stay for the time being as I was still too small to run for a long time and leave the jungle.

We hid during the day and were cautious during the night. My parents also trained me as a young foal to be careful.

We never left our home meadow and the jungle, and so I grew up without any other unicorns to play with.

I was lonely, and I was so delighted when I met a male White Horse.

When the White Horse abandoned me and his foal, I was heartbroken. My parents had already passed away when he left us, so I was all on my own with my little foal.

The sad story of the Unicorn moved the Rainbow. Now he understood even more how precious the Unicorn was in the jungle. She had suffered greatly, and yet she was so happy and content with who she was, and she took good care of her little foal.

The Rainbow felt accepted by the Unicorn for who he was. She was unique, and she embraced his uniqueness, even though they were so different.

After he heard the tale of the unicorns, he thought that she might be the only one who could bring him happiness after what he had experienced in the past.

The Unicorn was different from those animals he had met before. She was kind, forgiving and caring, and so pure in heart.

'Please tell me your story, Rainbow,' the Unicorn asked him after she finished her story.

'Why can the animals not see the end of the Rainbow? It seems as if you are hiding it. I do not understand that.

'I want to understand who you really are, because unicorns want to understand those they love. It does not matter if the other has flaws or weaknesses. We unicorns want to see only their true inner being,' the Unicorn explained to the Rainbow.

She felt that the Rainbow was hiding his inner self from her. How could she love him if she did not know who he really was? But then she also felt that it was worth the risk of loving him even if she did not know his whole story.

'It is hard to open up, as I have already been disappointed twice by those I loved. But I will tell you my story so that you understand better why the animals cannot see the end of the Rainbow,' he replied.

Once, I was together with a beautiful Black Horse. I loved the Black Horse dearly, but she was always away, running after gold and collecting it. She placed the gold she collected at my end so that I could protect it.

I also started collecting gold, which I shared with her. But because I was busy searching for gold, and she was busy finding it, we did not see each other very much. I often missed the Black Horse, but I knew that I had to make sure that she was happy, and so I continued to collect gold.

One day, I came back to the meadow earlier than planned. I had found lots of gold and was happy that I would be able to surprise her, but the Black Horse was displeased when she saw me.

I did not know why she was so angry. I always wanted to make her happy, but lately, she had always been miserable.

I could not make things right with her—she always complained that I had done something wrong in her eyes.

Hence, I had wanted to surprise her by coming back to the meadow quicker than she expected. I thought that she would be happy if I came back earlier than anticipated, but I felt that she was not.

The Black Horse excused herself at noon. She said that she wanted to run to a distant meadow and spend the day and the night in that meadow with her friend, the female Brown Horse.

I was sad that she did not want to spend the day with me, but I accepted it. Deep down inside me, though, something did not feel right; something made me suspicious. My intuition was screaming at me.

I was a little jealous that I was a rainbow and not a horse. So I asked my friend, the White Falcon, to see where the Black Horse was going.

The Falcon came back early the next morning and told me what he had seen.

The Black Horse had met a male Grey Horse. First they had eaten grass together in the meadow, then they had lain in the meadow and the Grey Horse had caressed the Black Horse, and then they had danced the night away.

They had laughed and made fun of me—how could I believe that a beautiful Black Horse like her could ever love a rainbow?

I was sad that the Black Horse had been unfaithful to me. I could no longer be with her. But because I still loved her very much, I gave her part of my gold.

The Black Horse left the meadow, and I was again alone, thinking that I might never find someone who would love me for who I am.

After many full moons had passed and I had forgotten my heartbreak over the Black Horse, I met the Golden Retriever.

The Golden Retriever also liked gold very much. She wanted to dig for gold herself, but because she was lazy, she never found any. She started to take the gold from the big pot that I had hidden at my end.

Finally, I realised that the Golden Retriever was only with me because of my gold.

I was again shattered, and I tried to hide the gold, but the Golden Retriever found it. She took from the pot as much gold as she could carry and fled before I could send a storm after her.

I was devastated. I decided that I would never again show the gold at my end to another animal and that I would hide in this meadow with its beautiful lake.

The only animal who came to this meadow from time to time was the Wise Owl, with whom I talked about my misfortunes in love. She helped me to understand that it was not I who was at fault, but the Black Horse and the Golden Retriever who had wronged me.

Tears formed in the Unicorn's eyes as she listened to the sad story of the Rainbow. She had been heartbroken when the White Horse left her, and she could feel that the Rainbow had suffered a lot, too.

She looked deep into his blue eyes, which he always showed to her to display his love. The Rainbow felt the compassion of the Unicorn.

'When I saw you for the first time as you entered my meadow, I felt how the energy changed here. Now I feel your warmth and your love for me, and that truly makes me happy,' the Rainbow said to her.

'I hope that you now understand why I do not show the other end of the Rainbow to any animal. I do not want anyone to come only for my gold,' he explained to her.

The Unicorn saw that he was terrified that someone might steal his pot of gold.

'I do not understand why this pot of gold is so important to you, Rainbow,' the Unicorn said. 'I know that many animals like gold because it shines so brightly. But to be honest, it really does not seem to add anything to their lives. They can eat the fresh grass of the meadow and drink the cold water of the lake. Why do they need more, and what do you need the gold for anyway?' she asked.

'But I have worked so hard forever and a day to find this gold. It shines so brightly, and the animals seem to like me when they see my gold,' the Rainbow replied.

'But you shine so much brighter than the gold, Rainbow,' the Unicorn burst out, obviously annoyed that the Rainbow could not see his own beauty.

'Your brilliance is worth more than a thousand pots of gold. You make other animals happy when you appear. And those who search for gold at the end of the Rainbow when they see you are simply not worth your time and consideration.

'You bring so much to this world by simply being yourself. I think you should start loving yourself so that you, too, can see that the greatest gift we possess is to love and accept ourselves as we are,' she said.

'I think that you are right, Unicorn. Thank you for loving me for who I am,' the Rainbow said, and his other end lit up.

The Unicorn could see the pot of gold, which the Rainbow had kept hidden before. But the Unicorn saw only his beauty. The Rainbow was so bright—much brighter than the pot of gold that was shimmering at his end. She kissed and hugged him, and suddenly he could feel that warm fuzzy feeling in his rainbow heart.

For the first time, he understood what true love is: to be accepted and loved for who we are and not for what we have.

The Red Fody looked around and searched the eyes of the young animals to see whether they were happy with the ending of the story.

'Oh, what a beautiful story. I will dream about the Unicorn and the Rainbow the whole night. That is how love should be. I wish that I could find someone like the Rainbow who lights up in his colours when I am around him and who sees my worth,' the beautiful Mountain Zebra burst out.

Every animal around the Flame Tree knew that she was madly in love with the Handsome Zebra but that he showed her little respect as his eyes were on numerous female zebras.

'I think that happy endings are boring. You hear exactly the ending that you expect. How could the Tigress, who suffered so greatly in her life, tell you a story that has such a mellow ending? Even the Mountain Zebra, who is hopelessly in love, now dreams of becoming a Unicorn who meets her Rainbow,' the cheeky Young Elephant burst out. Many of the young animals around him laughed and nodded.

'I did not say that this was the end of the story. I just hoped that I could finish here and you would go home. But I see now that you are clever as you realised that this was not the end,' the Red Fody sighed. She had seriously hoped that the young animals would have had enough.

'I, too, initially thought that this was the end of the fairy tale as I was so madly in love with the Giant Eagle at that time. When we are in love, we want good things to happen, and often we ignore the fact that the reality looks completely different. You were right: the story of the Unicorn and the Rainbow continued, and it had a couple of twists.

'I will tell you the rest of the fairy tale when you come back tomorrow. You must all go now. I need to sleep.

'One of these days, I may also tell you how the brave animals of the Tiny Island saved the ocean around the island. You may also want to know what happened to the two coconut shells that were buried at the Energy Point of the South,' the Fody chirped.

'You only ever told us the story of the Tigress because it was your favourite story, but you seem to know many more tales! How come you remember these stories all of a sudden?' the cheeky Young Elephant asked and laughed.

But his question remained unanswered as the ancient Red Fody was already far up in the crown of the Flame Tree, not hearing the question of the Young Elephant or not wanting to hear it.